Voices over the horizon

Tales from Cable & Wireless

Voices over the horizon

Tales from Cable & Wireless

David Souden

GRANTA EDITIONS

CABLE AND WIRE

ESS VIA IMPERIAL

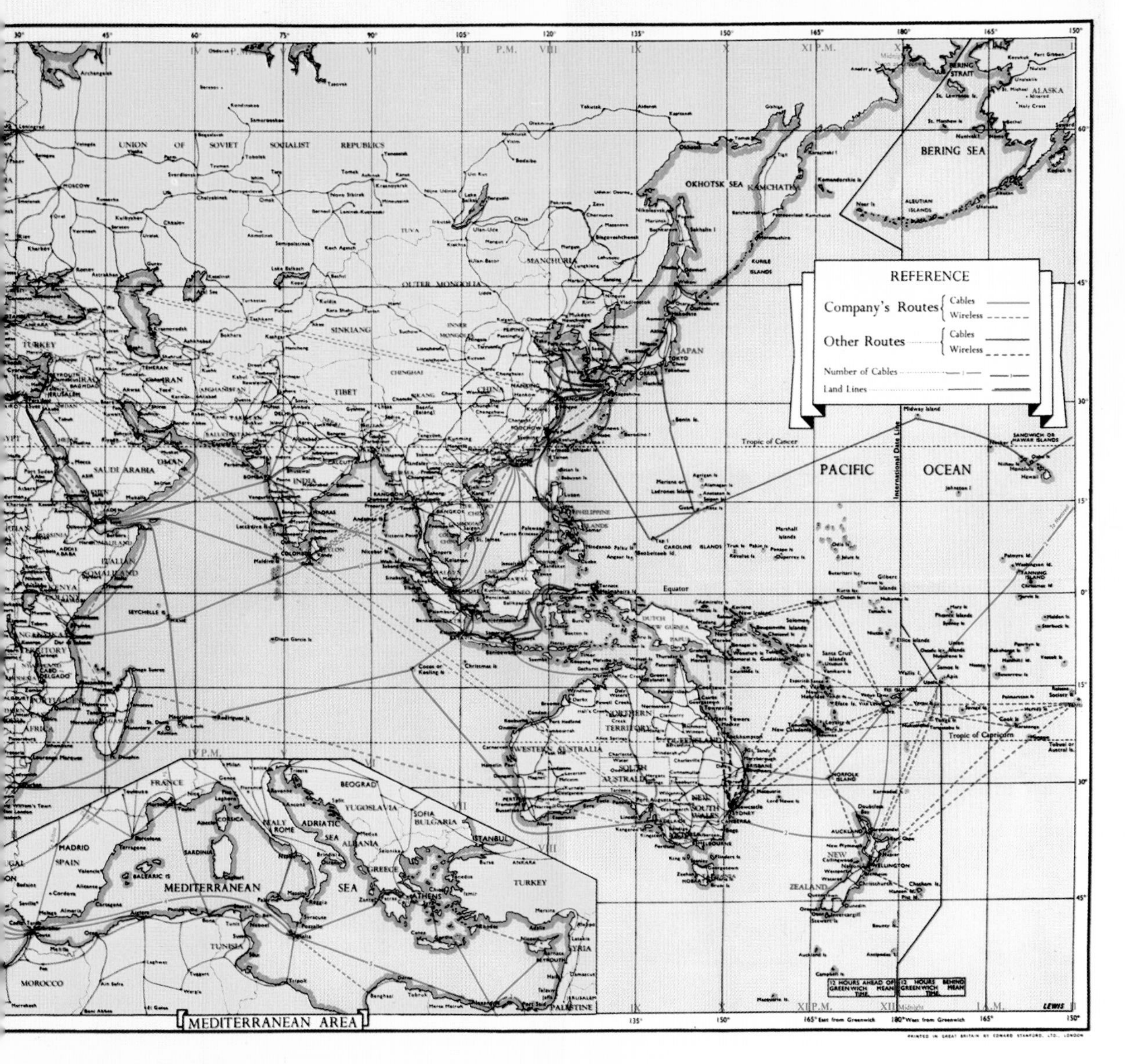

Published by Granta Editions, 25–27 High Street, Chesterton, Cambridge CB4 1ND, United Kingdom.

Granta Editions is a wholly owned imprint of Book Production Consultants plc

First published in 1999.

A CIP catalogue record for this book is available from the British Library.

ISBN 1 85757 067 7

Picture acknowledgements

The author and publishers are grateful to the following for lending illustrations and giving permission to reproduce the following:

Ted Amor, pp.41, 42, 58–59, 109 (and cover design); Wendy Suart, pp.44, 172;
Peter Critchley, p.116; John Bragg, p.153; Hulton Getty, pp.151, 259

All other pictures are from the Cable & Wireless Archives.

Every effort has been made to obtain permission for the reproduction of the illustrations and photographs in this book; apologies are offered to anyone whom it has not been possible to contact.

Designed by Peter Dolton.
Design, editorial and production in association with
Book Production Consultants plc, 25–27 High Street, Chesterton,
Cambridge CB4 1ND, United Kingdom.
Reprographics in Great Britain by Z2, Thetford, Norfolk, United Kingdom.
Printed and bound in Great Britain by Jarrold Book Printers, Thetford, Norfolk, United Kingdom.

CONTENTS

Foreword ix

Preface xi

Introduction xv

Chapter One 1
Joining

Chapter Two 33
The way it was – Life at the cable stations

Chapter Three 113
Island life: Ascension and Cocos

Chapter Four 131
War

Chapter Five 155
Out with the old – New technology, new ways

Chapter Six 223
Hong Kong and China

Chapter Seven 245
In extremity – Political and natural upheaval

Chapter Eight 265
Over the horizon

Glossary 269

Interview material 273

Bibliography 274

Index 275

A GIRDLE ROUND THE EARTH
OVERSEAS
TELEGRAMS
CABLE AND WIRELESS
LIMITED
C AND W
One of the few organisations which, over a long period of years and in spite of wars, have steadily increased the facilities they afford to the public and reduced their charges for them.

FOREWORD

In a glass case on a landing on the second floor of the company's headquarters in London is a large painting: the Cable & Wireless Great Circle Map. At the top of the picture are airy clouds, with seagulls swooping over tall transmission masts. Curving waves, teeming with multi-coloured fish, sport at the foot. Six roundels show: the S.S. *Great Eastern* (1865); a cable-loading operation; a wireless transmitter; a modern cable-ship, smoke billowing from the funnel (the picture was painted in 1945); cable transfer gear; and four men, in hot-weather kit, tapping out Morse Code at a mobile telegraph station. An open window (the artist's name, McDonald Gill, written above) gives on to shimmering, tropical blue.

The Great Circle, in the centre, is mostly ocean, the land masses strikingly projected, as if the viewer were gazing straight down from the heavens. From Britain (also Great), in the very middle, radiate the cable and the wireless links, joining continents and islands, sea, earth and sky. It is a romantic vision – and a romantic story. Enabling so many countries to send and receive invisible messages across thousands of miles was indeed, in words cited in this book, 'the closest thing to magic'.

What did those who commissioned Gill's map understand by the Great Circle? The navigational term, the mariners' Great Circle, passing through the Greenwich meridian? Or the girdle that by the end of the Second World War Cable & Wireless had put around the Earth? Gill's interpretation is inspired, teasing sober-suited directors, comforting investors, delighting stargazers.

Or were the cable-layers and signallers, engineers and operators – and the managers and administrators, despatching furniture, spare parts and instructions – were they themselves the Great Circle, whose networks, local and global, are the basis of the company today?

Listen to their voices, connecting across the years ...

Janet Morgan
Non-Executive director of Cable & Wireless

PREFACE

When I was first approached to work on this book, I was perhaps not alone in this country in understanding little more about Cable & Wireless than that it was somehow concerned with the Mercury telephone account I had. Even during the course of this project, the Company's public profile in Britain and elsewhere has been raised by its branding strategies and corporate expansion, and that greater visibility looks set to continue. Meanwhile, I came to understand what made this Company's history special, and what particular and individual qualities the people who worked for it had. As I explain in the introduction below, one of the intellectual elements I was keen to grapple with (having had an academic interest in the subject of population migration) was to understand more about expatriate life and why it was usually ignored, why there was so little written about it. That is one strand. This book is more than a history of expatriate life: living and working abroad forms the backbone, but there is also a fascinating history of technological and corporate change. Above all, there are voices. If I have done my job properly, the reader should be able to hear people talking in his or her head.

I am most grateful to Cable & Wireless for their invitation to undertake this project. Rod Olsen, who has been at various times Acting and Deputy Chief Executive, conceived the book. He together with Dr Janet Morgan, a non-executive Director of the Company and a distinguished historian in her own right, and Mary Godwin, Curator for Cable & Wireless, have guided and overseen the project, and they have generously allowed me to expand its scope both in the number of interviews and the size of the resulting publication. Many people at Cable & Wireless have been of great help in suggesting people for me to speak to and providing help, notably Gertude Gerstle, the former Archive Assistant, and Lisa Marriott who organised my overseas travel. Dick Brown, former Chief Executive, and Adrian Moorey, former Director of Corporate Communications, provided advice on direction at a critical juncture. My first research and interview trip was to Porthcurno where, like many before and since, I was drawn into the world of the submarine cables by the enthusiasm of the volunteers and professionals who run and manage the Museum there in the Tunnels.

I was introduced to Cable & Wireless by Stephanie Zarach and Book Production Consultants. This is the third occasion that I have worked with her and them, and I have always thoroughly enjoyed the experience.

Many people have been of immense assistance to me. Above all, I am grateful to all those who permitted me to come to talk to them about their lives and careers. Their names are listed separately, and an individual's name is attached to each quotation in the book. I have been magnificently received and entertained in many parts of Britain and other countries. For some people, after the initial shock that I actually wanted to hear their stories of life with the Company, the experience seems to have been something of an emotional release.

The most difficult task of all has been to decide what to include and what to exclude. Many people told fascinating stories that did not find a place in the final scheme, and I apologise in advance to those who are sorry not to see their own favourite anecdote included in this selection. The shortest interview was perhaps one and a half hours, the longest eleven hours. Each interview was taped (and later transcribed), and those tapes will be lodged in the Cable & Wireless archives. Some people showed me personal photographs, and have allowed me to reproduce them here. Wendy Suart generously permitted me to borrow and reproduce extracts from a taped interview by Radio Hong Kong with her late husband Brian in 1972.

My wife, Nicola, provided me with support and advice throughout, and bore my absences on interview trips stoically.

It must be borne in mind that, as the introduction suggests, memory is a fickle thing. Since this is a book almost wholly based on memory, some of that fickleness will almost certainly have come through. Some things remain the personal opinion or the particular memory of the individual, but wherever possible I have tried to check factual matters and compare accounts of the same event. Above all, this is a set of voices from the past of Cable & Wireless, with stories and experiences to be savoured.

INTRODUCTION

It is a curious fact that despite the vast extent of British involvement with other parts of the world, imperial and commercial, in the course of the nineteenth and twentieth centuries, there is remarkably little written about those who worked overseas, and about their lives abroad. There are honourable exceptions to that rule, but they exist more often in fiction than in the record of fact. The short stories of Somerset Maugham, or the Raj Quartet telling tales of Britain's later years in India, spring to mind. (There seems to be only one novel directly inspired by life with Cable & Wireless, Duff Hart-Davis's *The Gold of St Matthew* of 1970, a thriller more than loosely based on Company life on Ascension Island.) It is almost the case that more attention is being paid now, when most of that world has vanished, than before: to take a few non-fiction examples, Simon Winchester's and, more recently, Harry Ritchie's books visiting the remaining outposts of empire, or Alexander Frater's travel book that retraces the Empire flying boat route. Charles Allen's books, discussed below, about life in India, Africa and Malaya, are among the most distinguished contributions to the history of the British abroad.

Yet Britain's reach into the wider world, through both commerce and colonialism, would have been impossible without men and women who were dedicated to spending a significant part of their lives overseas. Most families in Britain would – one, two, three generations ago – have had at least one family member whose working life (or a significant part of it) was expatriate. In some families, expat 'dynasties', most members had a career abroad, in the armed forces, police and colonial services, or in commercial companies.

Perhaps it is not difficult to explain why there should have been that seeming indifference. For the most part, by working abroad expatriates had apparently defined themselves out of home society; their lives did not impinge on the lives of those who stayed behind, and their experiences were removed from general everyday life. Cable & Wireless employees *did* include those who got to work by paddling a boat, who spent six months almost alone on a deserted island in the Indian Ocean, or who woke to breathtaking views of palm trees and beaches. Those who had deep tans long before they were fashionable, and for whom native bearers brought pink gins at sundown. Moreover, expatriates often found that they could not fit back easily into British society: the country they knew had changed each time they returned after three or four years away, and nobody else really seemed to want to know what had happened that time they were last in Aden.

Although there are elements of caricature in this image of expatriate life, it is into such a system of overseas working that Cable & Wireless once fitted – and out of which system that the much-altered present-day Company has emerged. In the pages that follow, the stories of many who experienced a working life with Cable & Wireless are recounted, in their own words. These tales stretch from the 1930s to the 1980s, from the period when Cable & Wireless was picking itself up as a private enterprise after years of depressed business conditions, through its lengthy period of public ownership, to the point at which its ownership was returned to the private sector. And from a period of near-monopoly control of communications in a colonial setting to the threshold of becoming a global telecommunications entity.

Among the stories and the experiences are those that recapture the ordinary, others the extraordinary. Some look back with nostalgia, some look forward with expectation. Some criticise, some celebrate. All contribute to the particular phenomenon that was, and is, Cable & Wireless.

CABLE & WIRELESS: A BRIEF HISTORY

The history of the companies that became Cable and Wireless plc began with the Manchester cotton industry in 1852, when the cotton merchant John Pender joined enterprises that would run a telegraph cable service between, first, London and Dublin and thereafter between England and the USA.

Information was the key to economic success, and over the course of the 1860s Pender – bitten by the information bug – created a series of companies that laid and operated cables successively to the Iberian peninsula, the Mediterranean and North Africa, to India, Hong Kong, Singapore, Australia, South America, and sub-Saharan Africa. By the end of the century Pender was the world's leading light in the cable business. His son, and subsequently his grandson, were in their turn to lead the constellation of companies that Pender had formed.

These early enterprises were all based upon submarine cables, along which telegraph messages were sent. The opening years of the twentieth century witnessed the advent of a competing system of telecommunication, radio. In 1901 Guglielmo Marconi succeeded in sending a signal across the Atlantic, and in the course of the following twenty-five years the rival systems, telegraph and radio, did battle for international communications. The short-lived boom of the Great War years was followed by long-term depression in the 1920s and into the 1930s, despite the technical advances that improved the accuracy of communications and automated many of the processes of transmission. In the course of those years of difficulty the interests of the Pender companies and the Marconi Company were eventually joined together. The merger, effected in 1929, produced the Cable & Wireless that remains recognisable to this day.

The system that Cable & Wireless operated was well-expressed in the name the principal operating company bore between 1929 and 1934: Imperial and International Communications. The extent of Britain's empire, and its commercial net around the world, underpinned its communications. In the course of the Second World War, in which both cable and radio communication played a critical role, Cable & Wireless provided paramilitary telecommunications units for many campaigns. Once the war was over, a reforming Labour government was elected, and following discussions with governments in independent territories within the Commonwealth – formerly the Empire – the company was taken into public ownership on 1 January 1947. Most of its assets and operations in the UK were transferred to the Post Office in

1950, yet Cable & Wireless remained the world's largest single international telegraphy enterprise.

Although radio links were crucial for communication in some parts of the world, for the most part Cable & Wireless was still based upon the web of underwater cables that had been its mainstay for almost a century. Some 186,000 miles of submarine cable were maintained, converging on the Cornish coastal station of Porthcurno. Telegraphy was, however, becoming increasingly obsolete in the 1950s. The introduction of coaxial cables and improved radio systems, with voice transmission, offered the chance to switch to telephone connections. In the 1960s, written communications by telex superseded the old system of telegrams, while the opening up of the skies by satellite communication provided another new range of technical and commercial opportunities.

In the meantime, the progressive dismantling of Britain's colonial structure combined with the wish of newly independent nations to take over some, if not all, of their external communications further squeezed old working patterns. Fewer expatriates were needed, as local-born people progressively took over their jobs. Massive investment was required, often with other commercial or political partners, yet the number of places in which the Company was active was shrinking. Hong Kong proved Cable & Wireless's lifeline; by the early 1970s its activities there had expanded enormously, and the Crown Colony provided five-sixths of the profits. Those profits were returned to the Treasury, while successive British governments' control of Cable & Wireless has been characterised as one of benign neglect rather than scrutiny.

At the end of the 1960s, Cable & Wireless had had to take a careful look at itself, deciding to branch out into many different forms of activity. Diversification was made more imperative by the loss of the Brazilian concessions after a century and ultimately the total disappearance of the Company from South America. In the course of the 1970s, the marketing of subsidiaries, the provision of dedicated communications networks, and specialist contracts (of which that for the Saudi Arabian National Guard was by far the largest and most important) paved the way for the most recent of the great changes that Cable & Wireless has undergone in the past twenty years.

The election of a Conservative government in 1979, under Margaret Thatcher, determined to privatise as much of the state-owned sector as it could and – as soon as it could – heralded the sale of the company in 1981. Half of the shares were offered then, and the remainder (except for a single government 'golden share') followed by 1985. It was a successful, and path-forming, privatisation. Hong Kong business remained paramount through the 1980s: the international licence was renewed in 1981, and the internal telephone company was acquired in 1984. Meanwhile, the Company under Sir Eric Sharp became far less dependent on governmental service concessions in various territories, and entered into a wider range of commercial undertakings. The most important fruit of that was Mercury, a second telecommunications service to compete against British Telecom in the UK.

Finally, Cable & Wireless was achieving full recognition in the country in which it was based. Since then, access has been gained to a wider range of markets, companies have been acquired and concessions gained in many parts of the world. In some cases, Cable & Wireless has been returning to places it had left a long time before; elsewhere, it has all been a fresh start. From a British imperial-based enterprise with one principal asset, its submarine cable network, Cable & Wireless has emerged as one of the world's most important and far-flung telecommunications companies.

HISTORY IN THE MEMORY

That is the corporate story of Cable & Wireless. Every business is composed of individuals, each with his or her own part to play in the enterprise. Some would have been blissfully unaware of the wider political and economic realities, others only too well aware. It is through those individuals and their memories that Cable & Wireless's story is told here, in selections from interviews recorded with many dozens of men and women who worked for Cable

& Wireless or who were associated with it. Their words convey the variety of forms of Company life, principally abroad but also to some extent at home in Britain.

Memory is a fragile thing. Humans are fallible beings: one person's immediate memory of an event may be quite different from somebody else's memory of the same event. Over time, individuals sift, rearrange, embellish, polish their memories. An essential question in pursuing the work for this book has been: can memories produce more than a distorted picture of the world?

The answer: memory is a unique way of recording everyday patterns and working practices, things that are rarely documented at the time and will vanish unless they are recovered. Memory is very poor at providing a reliable chronological narrative: individuals sometimes have difficulty in remembering what they did, and in what order, last week or last month, let alone almost a lifetime away. Yet age and the chance to reflect on a lifetime's events may prove a much more reliable guide: short-term memory is notoriously more fickle in those of advancing years than is long-term memory. What was once novel may have become prosaic – but that need not diminish the memory of the excitement and wonder of the novelty. For an individual's memory is just that, individual. Someone who is caught up in an event may have a wholly different perspective from the main or received one. There are many examples of that in this volume, from the experiences of those who found themselves inside a momentous political event to a chance encounter or a single occasion that has left a lasting impression.

As much as possible, the memories that have been tapped for this book are recounted through individuals' own words. Some raconteurs tell stories at length. Others offer nuggets of memory and wisdom. The organisation of the stories they tell is therefore crucial.

There are two critical elements in recalling Cable & Wireless's history: the chronological and the topical. There are two major chapters, the longest sections in this book, that provide some detail behind the corporate history and, more importantly, recall what it was like to live and work in the 1940s and 1950s, and then in the 1960s and 1970s. Five subsidiary chapters explore particular themes. First, how people came to join the Company. In some cases the tradition of service was in their family, in other cases the chance to travel and have a technological career beckoned. Then, what was life and work like on a remote island or amid the bustle of Hong Kong? Finally, how did people cope in adversity? – in war, during political upheaval or when Nature was trying to do its worst? Most of the people who tell their stories here are retired foreign service staff and their families, now returned to their native Britain; others hardly ever left these shores, or are among those native to a particular location and who now occupy positions that were once reserved for expatriates.

ORAL HISTORY

This book is based upon interviews recorded in 1997 and 1998 with some ninety individuals. This text has been derived from an archive something in the order of two million words. The goal has been to organise the material so that the overall story emerges, with occasional editorial prompts, but individuals shine through. Therefore, although speech has been 'tidied up' to make it possible to read, for the most part stories are reproduced verbatim, pithy or lengthy as the circumstances and the speaker dictate.

Various earlier oral histories have been guiding lights for this project. One of the most important contributions to 'popular' oral history are the three volumes that Charles Allen published, based on radio talk series, between 1975 and 1983, *Plain Tales from the Raj*, *Tales from the Dark Continent* and *Tales from the South China Seas.* These tapped memories of the colonial worlds in India, Africa and South-East Asia, worlds peopled with District Commissioners, policemen and missionaries, rubber and tea planters. The academic practice of oral history in Britain has been associated above all with work based in the University of Essex under the leadership of Paul Thompson, whose book *The Voice of the Past* has been both a powerful advocate and also a practical guide for oral history. The methods and the end results are quite different, but the work of Tony Parker has also been of importance in shaping this book. His publications have been principally, although far from exclusively, concerned with aspects of the criminal justice system. An interviewee is described in a few telling words, and interviews are reproduced seemingly verbatim. With few prompts from the author, pictures and voices enter the reader's head.

Although a project of this nature has its antecedents, it must also have its own character. And here the character is determined by the Company and the people it took on. One of the people interviewed for this book said that 'Cable & Wireless types' were distinguished more by what they did not say than by what they did say. Even if that were true, they still (as these pages show) have a great deal to say.

CHAPTER ONE

Joining

It was the travel part that decided me – nothing much to do with the technology. I said fine, I'll do it. I went down to London, had my examinations and tests, and that is how I joined Cable & Wireless. As simple as that.

Colin Sharp

Cable & Wireless principally recruited young men in order to train them for a life working abroad, maintaining and managing its many operational bases. It also had a key staff in its London headquarters. Substantial numbers of telegraph operators, telegram messengers and office counter staff, eventually to be followed by technical and managerial personnel, were recruited from the international location.

The Company's expatriate foreign service staff often had careers that took them to wholly different places around the globe, from remote Amazonia to bustling Hong Kong or from a Pacific atoll to West Africa. They had to be able to cope with both the pressures of loneliness on remote islands, and with working hard and playing hard in a lively tourist destination. The men's training was conducted at first in London and subsequently, from the early 1950s, in the remote Cornish village of Porthcurno, near Lands End, the place where the overseas telegraph cables all came ashore.

Marrying was frowned upon until these men had established themselves, when they were well into their twenties. They had to be prepared to move wherever and whenever the Company sent them. It was a way of life that some fell into by accident, while others came to work for Cable & Wireless through family connections. It was a rude shock, the opportunity of a lifetime, or sometimes both, as their individual stories tell.

As time has passed, and especially as technology has changed, so the training required of personnel has altered radically. A generation or two ago, most people joining Cable & Wireless expected to spend their working lives with the Company. The substantial numbers of staff permanently based overseas have now largely disappeared, as have the types of foreign station that they lived and worked in. London-based operations have become commercially of far greater importance, although the nature of the centre's tight control over overseas locations has altered. Life in the Company's locations around the world has changed so radically since the 1940s, and yet it is that far-flung global network that still underpins the workings of Cable & Wireless to this day.

Pete Wolfe *joined in 1938 when recruitment began again after the depression of the 1930s and the mass laying-off of personnel because of technological change. He was soon to be plunged into wartime work.*

I come from the East End of London, and my father was [a telegraph] operator for Cable & Wireless in London. He was the fastest operator they had. One day he came home and said that the Company announced that they had new vacancies. They hadn't recruited much for a long time, and now after the slump was over they were starting again. I said to my dad, 'I don't want to go to be an operator like you,' and he said, 'No, this is purely engineering. Good pay, they give you all the training; you'll go abroad, have a lovely life.' And I said, 'All right, I'll go for interview,' and I was the first non-public school boy accepted for foreign service. That was 1938 ...

All my colleagues were public school. We went to the training school, that was then at the top of Hampstead Hill [north London]. They introduced us to each other and they said, 'Right, sit down and learn the Morse Code.' So I went home to my father that night and I said, 'You conned me.' He said, 'What do you mean?' 'First thing they said was sit down and learn the ruddy Morse Code!' So he said, 'Every night from now on you sit down and do an hour's practice with me. You're not letting my reputation as an operator down.' I let myself right in for it. I never got above twenty words a minute, but that was sufficient.

They taught us touch-typing, Morse Code; we had to do all the operating side plus engineering. We had six months in the workshop learning how to make tools and all that, and we had to make our own tool-kit including taps and dies. From scratch. And we were also given sheets of brass, two inches square, and we had to file them to within two thousandths of an inch. Measured with a micrometer all over. Then we had to cut a cross out, and that was all measured. Then we had to make two pieces of brass interlinking and they had to fit in. And if you could get a 2 mm feeler gauge in anywhere [your work was] rejected. It took us about a fortnight to make that damn thing. At the end of it they were all either passed or rejected – and then they put a pair of shears through them. We weren't allowed to keep them. I could have killed the workshop instructor. He said, 'You're not handing them on to the next batch' ...

When the war broke out they decided that the Post Office wanted our training school so they moved us into [the Cable & Wireless offices at] Moorgate. Then in 1941 the Germans bombed the Moorgate office, the Tower Chambers end, and destroyed all our training school. We lost all our notes and equipment and stuff, and they then put us into Head Office, Electra House on Victoria Embankment. We were there renewing all our notes and everything else and then after a few weeks they said, 'Right, we've got nothing to train you with, you can go abroad and finish your training, learn your job abroad.' A pal and I were transferred to Ascension Island [in the South Atlantic]. We were in convoy at three knots for four weeks. We then left the convoy with three other ships, and later we were told that those three were sunk the same night. We got through. We were on the old *Gloucester Castle*, which was about 7,000 tons, and her flat-out speed was about seven knots. But we got to Ascension all right.

John Howie *now lives in La Paz. Much of his working life with the Company was to be spent in South America.*

My father was a naval officer, and I wanted to see the world, having seen all the mementoes that he had brought back. My mother was in the Company: she was the Traffic Manager's secretary. Various uncles were

Electra House, Embankment, London, 1946

NO ENTRY
DISMANTLERS
WMAN & Co. Ltd
CLK
183

involved in the old 'Eastern', as I found out later from a cousin when I went back to England. My cousin was working in the International Operations department, and he told me that he had calculated I was the thirteenth or the fourteenth member of the family to be in the Company. He reckoned it was a record. But I was the only one who was, shall we say, a 'useful' member; all the others were administrative Head Office staff.

The family connection wasn't mentioned when I went for interview. I had to take an entrance examination, and to show that I knew one end of a screwdriver from another, that sort of thing. If I remember rightly, I was asked to adjust a set of fork sounders which we used to use in those days, and general knowledge – where various parts of the world were – and some mathematics, and whether I could read and write. And that was it. Before my time, I believe, you were taken on if you were a good rugger player or if you could play good cricket, and you were posted according to where they needed someone to play cricket or rugby. But when I joined it was more 'intellectual'.

There were probably about ten or fifteen in my group. There were some that disappeared – I don't know what happened to them. In our group there was a guy who used to do all his metalwork wearing gloves, because he was a pianist. He must have left the Company eventually ...

The thing for which I'm always grateful to the Company is that they taught me how to use a keyboard ... Also, we were taught to use hand perforators, that I never saw again after I left the training school: three little steel buttons and you thumped them. There was a guy who came back from Cuba, and he showed us how he could hand-punch. He was fantastic – *chung-chung-chung-chung-chung* with these little metal hammers, and the paper tape was just flying out for a foot before it fell on the ground. He was incredible.

Two years, three years training. We went to Porthcurno – for settling in to work in an actual station. Then we were thrown out into the cold hard world.

Paul Foster *is Barbadian. He joined in 1942 but subsequently left Cable & Wireless to become a journalist and then promoter of tourism on the island.*

In those days in Barbados when you left school the avenues of employment were rather limited. If you were lucky you got a job at one of the banks, and I suppose in second position was Cable & Wireless. The reason for that was the banks had far more opportunities for employment, Cable & Wireless was then rather narrow. My friend Arthur Farmer and I were both 17 years old, around that age.

Arthur Farmer *also subsequently left the Company, but remains active in amateur radio in Barbados, running a weather service.*

Paul Foster and I turned up together on 2 August 1942, and I was a little bit disappointed. When I went for my interview at the cable station there seemed to be such a lot of activity up there, but when I was told to report to the Reef [the town station in Bridgetown] there was only one wireless operator on duty, and one cable operator. I thought this really isn't very exciting. I thank my lucky stars that Paul and I worked together for quite a number of months on the verandah, learning to type, teaching one another Morse and very shortly afterwards a school was set up at Cable & Wireless. Monthly, thereafter, other operators came in who were to be trained in wireless: manual wireless, automatic wireless. Then we were sent for a time to the cable station at St Lawrence to learn the cable.

Maurice Bane *was one of the substantial number recruited in 1942. After the standard variety of postings, mainly in North Africa and the Far East, he stayed in Manila as General Manager for the Philippines for many years before retiring in 1982.*

I got up to London, didn't quite know where to stay. I was a very keen Sea Scout, so I stayed on the *Discovery*, Captain Scott's ship by the Temple, right opposite the Cable & Wireless building. I slept for a few weeks in Captain Scott's cabin. My great hero as a child was Scott, and also [T.E.] Lawrence – you know how you get schoolboy heroes – so being on the *Discovery* was absolutely marvellous. Everyone else had to travel, and I just walked across the road.

When we joined there were about sixteen in our group. We joined on £39 a year, so we were supported by our parents, we couldn't do otherwise. They had to sign a guarantee that if for any reason I dropped out from the London Training School, then the expenses and costs up to that time would have to be reimbursed ... It was a very Victorian scene really in many ways.

We were taken on the staff after one year and the salary went to £110 a year. We were all then called to see Sir Edward Wilshaw. He was a figure of awe. You were never allowed through the front entrance of Cable & Wireless, that was only for the senior people – you went down a little side alley. Wilshaw would turn up in his carriage and horses. This splendid carriage came along, a chap with a big whip, postilion at the back, stopped outside the front door, the postilion would go round and open the door and out would step Sir Edward Wilshaw. He was hoping to be Lord Mayor of London, he was working towards that. He was our great chief. As far as we were concerned we were the lowest of the low, and he was way up there.

So we were called to his office: he had a large office, with an enormous map of the world, and we all lined up there. He said, 'Well, young men, you've now been taken on the staff of Cable & Wireless, and you realise that you're going to be ambassadors for us overseas, and we shall expect you to behave according to all the patterns, and you will go to very many exciting

Night and day
minute by minute
the telegraph stations
of Cable and Wireless
are sending and receiving
vital messages—
words of happiness
words of drama
words of trade
Communications
THE LIFE-BLOOD OF CIVILIZATION
CAREER SECTION

places.' He started going across this map of the world. One of our chaps was prone to fainting, and he suddenly fainted on the carpet. Old Sir Edward, in his pinstripes and his lovely jacket and tie, looked over and, seeing this chap on the floor, pressed a bell on his desk. A couple of girls came in – he had stunning secretaries, all in St John's Ambulance uniforms – and said, 'This young man appears to have been overcome by being in my presence. Will you take him away?'

George Warwick *eventually achieved his early ambition of running the Company's operations in Hong Kong. He retired as General Manager there in 1981.*

People were talking about me going into a bank or whatever. That all seemed very dull. My brother suggested, why didn't I get a job as he had with Cable & Wireless, who send people overseas? That sounded good. I made my application, went up and took the test, had the interviews, and was told I could start in May. May 1943 ...

Basically, the training was with the technology that was in use at the time. When you look back it was so terribly crude it just wasn't true. You did go off to some fairly remote places, and a lot of the equipment was mechanical, so there was a fair amount of effort put into mechanical training and adjustment, and making small parts. You could end up that if you didn't have a spare and you couldn't make it, the whole place would pack up ... Cables were all there was then. They didn't really teach many people about radio. This was 1943 and radio communication was still quite a small part. It blossomed forth soon after the war, but before that cables were the major thing. Yet it seemed to a few of us that life *was* going to change, and in that respect we were right. Just a few months later the Company sent me on a course to the Marconi College at Chelmsford for a six-months' radio course. But that was just about the end of the war.

Pamela Aylmore *joined the Head Office staff in 1944, and she rose to become the first woman Chief Clerk of the Company. She spent her career in London and only went overseas briefly towards the end of a career that was truncated by illness.*

In 1944 I was fortunate enough to get a [secretarial] diploma ... My mother came down with me to see the Headmaster: 'We've just had a request from Cable & Wireless at Electra House on the Embankment, and they're looking for a young lady.' So on the Friday, which was 21 March 1944, I went for an interview. We got there at 9 o'clock, and I was met by a Mr Hitchcock. He gave me three pieces of correspondence in shorthand and I had to get it back, and he also gave me a long report to type and I went to the typing pool and I got them done by about 12 o'clock. 'Right, if you'd like to go to lunch, we'll have a look at this and see what we can do this afternoon.'

My mother in the meantime had come up out of the cold, it was a bitterly cold March day, the wind was blowing a treat, and they'd given her coffee and a French book to read – which we thought was quite amusing, as she didn't read any French, and I certainly didn't.

When we went back they gave me a huge sheet of figures. They really had a day's work out of me. I can see it now, it was 10 columns long, and 20 across, and all figures all the way along. It took me quite some while to set it out. It was one of those big old typewriters, we didn't have word processors or computers in those days, and the carriage was 29 inches long. I worked at this and got it finished by about half past three, quarter to four. Then I was taken to see the Traffic Manager, he looked at the work I'd done and said, 'Yes, I think that is very satisfactory.' He looked at everything else, I was asked various questions, and he said, 'Well, we're prepared to offer you the job, Miss Aylmore, providing you can start on Monday.' ...

I came through the hallowed doors at the front and walked into the Staff Department; I was then taken up to the fourth floor which was the Traffic Department, and I was put in with three elderly gentleman. One was a Mr Pearmain, 82, and Mr Norfolk – remember the war was on and these were all the people who had come back to help the Company out – who was 78, and then the young gentleman, Mr Evans. I think he was only 71. With these three gentlemen was a lady whose husband was a prisoner of war in Japan ...

There I settled down. At that time Cable & Wireless only employed single ladies. If you got married you had to leave, and so there were very few of us. The end of the Japanese war came, and Mrs Bennett left because her husband had come back from being a Japanese prisoner of war. Which left me with these three elderly gentlemen. I was called in by [my boss], and he said, 'I'm afraid we're going to have to move you.' 'Aren't you satisfied with what I do?' 'Oh,' he said, 'certainly I'm satisfied – but we couldn't *possibly* have a young lady on her own, in with three gentlemen in one office.' So I was taken out of there and put into the typing pool.

Colin Stubbs *was a member of the wartime Australasian contingent, recruited to provide communications for the latter stages of the war in the Far East. He made the Company his career thereafter, eventually becoming Head of the Staff Department in London. He now lives outside Sydney.*

In lots of ways Australia feels like home, but when you think about it, where is home when you have travelled the world most of your life? I started when I was two, but that's another story. I was born in Auckland. My father had been in the Pacific Cable Board, the PCB, which merged with Cable & Wireless. Then he worked for Overseas Telecommunications, OTC, the Australian company ... We went to Fiji [twice] before I joined the Company myself. So I hadn't been in one place for more than two or three years in my entire life until I got to England.

I wanted to be an architect before I joined the Company. I don't know what it was: my father brought home from the city a bit about Cable & Wireless wanting to recruit youngsters, and something happened. I changed my mind and went for Cable & Wireless. I joined at 16 – too young to be called up – and left Auckland to go to Colombo when I was probably just gone 18.

We were taken on just for the rest of the war, and nobody really thought that we would go on right through, in my case to the end. Of us all, of the twenty-two Kiwis, I was the last to leave the Company. I found it a great company ... We had a fantastic training. We had a guy called Jock Baird, who was in charge, and a chap called Dicky Heeps, the number two. Dicky Heeps would enthral us all with stories of life overseas: one which I haven't forgotten to this day was shooting tigers off the verandah of the office in Banjawoengie [in Indonesia]. We thought this was fantastic ... We learned a lot of sports through him, he taught us other things than just telecommunications. I carry the scars to this day – my best friend there broke my nose in a boxing lesson. I can remember Jock spent hours laboriously typing out an index card of short cablese with little guidelines for each one of us, individually, to take care of the future. One stuck in my mind: Learn to drink. It was about knowing *when to say No*, but you never forgot the bit about learning to *drink* which is probably a bit unfair.

Paul Carrington *can trace his ancestry in Barbados back to the 1650s. Having joined as an operator, he eventually became the first local staff member in Cable & Wireless's history to become General Manager of a station.*

I joined as a telegraph operator, they had a training school in Barbados at the time. I went through the training period, and then I continued as a telegraph operator until the late 1940s. Towards the end of the 1940s I was transferred to St Lucia after they'd had a large fire there, with Paul Foster. It was the days of the old ring telephone, and one evening I picked up the telephone and I heard this gibberish. I called Paul and asked him what it was all about. 'Oh, that's amateur radio.' 'What's that?' 'Well, you know, it's people talking to other people all over the world.' He phoned the exchange and asked if they knew where this chap was located. 'Yes, he's actually operating in our building.' He'd come over from Grenada to help with the emergency communications. We went down there and met him, and I got hooked with this thing.

I came back to Barbados and contacted a chap who was working on the technical side of the Company; he passed on to me a lot of technical information and I started to do some studying on my own. A couple of years later, in 1950 or so, I went to ask Pete Lawson, who was in charge of the two wireless stations in Barbados, if he had a particular valve. 'What do you want it for?' I told him I was a radio ham. 'Come into my office.' We sat down and had a chat: he asked me to describe my equipment, why I did this and that. After speaking to him for about an hour, he said, 'You're wasting your time, report to the transmitting station tomorrow,' and that's how I became an instant radio technician.

Ted Amor *lives in Devon. His technical skills and intuition were to take him, usually on short trouble-shooting stints, to almost every corner of the globe. He joined at the very start of 1945.*

They assumed that sooner or later you were going to be a Branch Manager or Branch Engineer, and you had to know everything that was going on ... I haven't used all the skills, but they have been invaluable. I knew everything that was going on at a station. Nobody could pull any wool over my eyes. That was the object of the training.

At the end of our training session, my friend Bob Darvill and I were waiting for our first postings, and we were called in and told we were going down to Porthcurno. Why? We were told, 'As you know we've been sending people down to Porthcurno for two months' consolidation [training in a real cable station] before they go overseas. Porthcurno has got fed up with this – no sooner have they got a man who can take the watch than he's whisked away. So they want some permanent ones. Eighteen months. You do what you're told ...'

After about a month consolidating we were put on the rounds as Assistant Engineers ... Eventually the old supervisors began to retire, and Bob and I were lumbered with the combined job of Supervisor/Assistant Engineer. After six months we were running the whole watch. In the biggest cable station in the world. So there's a young man of 21 in charge of this huge set-up – it opens your eyes a bit.

Albert Lorens *acquired British citizenship after getting out of the new state of Israel where he had become a stateless person. He had a technical career inside the Company, and now lives in Cornwall.*

Probably my accent puzzles you. I was born in Palestine. I was of European parentage – French and Italian – and I am British. I was actually born there and started with the Company in Haifa [in 1947]. I must have been about 16. It was just someone in the street from the same school: his brother was already in [the Company], and he said they were looking for someone to work there, would I join Cable & Wireless? So I went and asked my parents. They said OK.

When I started, actually, I started as a messenger. They had better bicycles than the one I'd got. I joined, and soon after that it seems the Manager found out that I could repair the bicycles better than anyone else; from there, they needed someone on the technical side and I accepted. Through books and so on I trained, did lots of homework. At first I used to have an exam every week, then every month. The Manager did not want to take any risks, I was with the same salary as I used to have, no increment or anything like that. He wanted to be sure that I was the right person for the job. So I was studying hard all the time, and I passed.

I worked in Haifa. I covered two other stations, Jaffa and Tel Aviv, and I used to travel specially to Tel Aviv, a bigger station. Every fortnight we'd service the equipment and then come back. I used to enjoy that, on a motorbike, going to Tel Aviv and back. At one time I couldn't go there any more because of fighting. Then I was stationed there. One of the British staff, F1 staff, used to travel in an armoured car to the office, and one day [terrorists] just put a bomb inside – from the top, because the top used to

The basic laboratory in the London Training School at Electra House before the school's move to Porthcurno

be open, it was only the sides that were armoured. The police said to the Company, 'Sorry, we cannot transport your staff any more.' So they asked me if I would go there: I was neutral, I wasn't British, not Arab, not Jewish, so I was OK.

Derek Moore *was recruited in 1948. Like most of his colleagues he spent his working life in different parts of the world, but his skills were put to different uses since he came to specialise in managing telephone systems.*

I don't think anyone ever asked me if I wanted to join Cable & Wireless – my father was in Cable & Wireless, my brother was. I think the principal requirement for anyone to join in those days was to have his ancestors in Cable & Wireless.

Howard Kleyn *became one of the two founding employees of the nascent Mercury Communications, after a career spent in many parts of the world.*

When I was released from the armed forces I went out to join my mother [who was working in Bermuda for Shell] and had a preliminary holiday in Bermuda. While I was there I observed groups of expats, British working overseas, and they were of course from the usual companies: Shell, naturally, Metal Box and Cable & Wireless. So I thought, this is good, an overseas life is the one for me. I came back to London and applied to join Cable & Wireless. This was now 1950. When I went for the interview I went through the usual procedures, answered the questions and so on, and at the end the interviewer said, 'Is there anything you wish to ask me?', and I said, 'No, I don't think so.' I had already seen the Company overseas, at least from its social aspect. So he said, 'Well now, tell me, Mr Kleyn, what is it that makes you wish to join Cable & Wireless?' Before I could stop myself I said, 'Well, actually, I first wanted to join Shell.' This amused him so much. I thought at the time that was the end of my career right at the first instant. The actual reason was that at the

Bermuda, complete with aerials and lily fields:
many a young recruit's first posting overseas

Shell interview I asked them if I could progress up through the company. They said, not up to the highest levels unless you have a degree in chemical engineering. Which I didn't have. I asked the same question at Cable & Wireless, and they said, you can go right up to Managing Director if you have the necessary qualities. So I thought to myself, at least it sounds more open ...

Looking back at it now, I think we can take a more balanced view: that the Company's recruiting policy was remarkably good and – whether it was based on rather foolish questions of the 'Do you play rugger?' kind or not – the fact of the matter remains that the number of staff who remained in the Company rather than dropping aside from the original recruitment was quite high for a company of that kind. We did develop some sort of corporate bond, which was highly necessary since each of us was working several hundred miles from the next one, right round the world.

John Davenport *eventually moved from the engineering to the management side; the last part of his career with the Company was spent running its operations in the USA.*

I was at school, I had just taken my O-levels, I hadn't got a clue what I wanted to do, except that my interests were science-related in the broadest possible sense. My sister came home one day with an advertisement cut out of the *Daily Telegraph* and in very large bold letters it said, **A CAREER ABROAD**. And in very much smaller print it said, IN TELECOMMUNICATIONS. The emphasis was on the career abroad and, well, all right, it was in telecommunications, but I think that [distinction] was quite significant.

On the strength of that I applied to Cable & Wireless and I was invited to Electra House on the Embankment, the headquarters of the Company in those days. They have knocked the building down now, but it was a very fine building with a substantial number of steps leading up to very large bronze doors. It was quite an imposing place. I remember going up those steps, and the door was opened by a commissionaire in full regalia. He asked me my business, and I told him. I went in, and went through the interview process which included some theoretical testing and some practical ability. Subsequently I was advised that I had been selected to join the training school. So on the first day, in early September 1953, I rushed up those self-same steps and the bronze door opened and there was the self-same commissionaire, and he asked me my business and I told him, and in no uncertain terms he told me that I had to go back down the steps and round to the back of the building. Students were not allowed in through the front door. That's always stuck in my mind for setting the scene for the first fifteen years – the first twenty years – of my life in Cable & Wireless. Because it was very much a hierarchical system, very paternal, took good care of you, *if* you played by the rules ...

Ron Werngren *lives in Cornwall close to many former Cable & Wireless employees, but he is of British-Argentinian extraction and his career was partly, although far from exclusively, spent in South America.*

I was born and brought up in Buenos Aires. I left there when I was 24. My education was at a British school, St Alban's College, which naturally had to follow the local curriculum, which we did in the morning in Spanish, while in the afternoon we did Cambridge School Certificate stuff. Finishing there at 15, I went along to the local secondary school for the *baccalaureate*, which I accelerated a little bit and finished when I was 19, and then went on to the Faculty of Engineering of the University of Buenos Aires. I didn't complete that course, because it was highly politicised. It was at the time of Perón, and I found it very uncomfortable. I couldn't really cope with it, I suppose. So I wandered around, got a job. I happened to say to a friend that I didn't like where I was working and was there a job in Western Telegraph? (That was what Cable & Wireless was called out in Buenos Aires.) There was, and I joined, on 1 August 1954.

And on 4 August 1954 I got on the *Brazil Star* and sailed back to what everybody called 'home' – although they may never have been there before. I came straight down to Porthcurno, and I was hooked ... It *was* like coming

Students swimming at Porthcurno

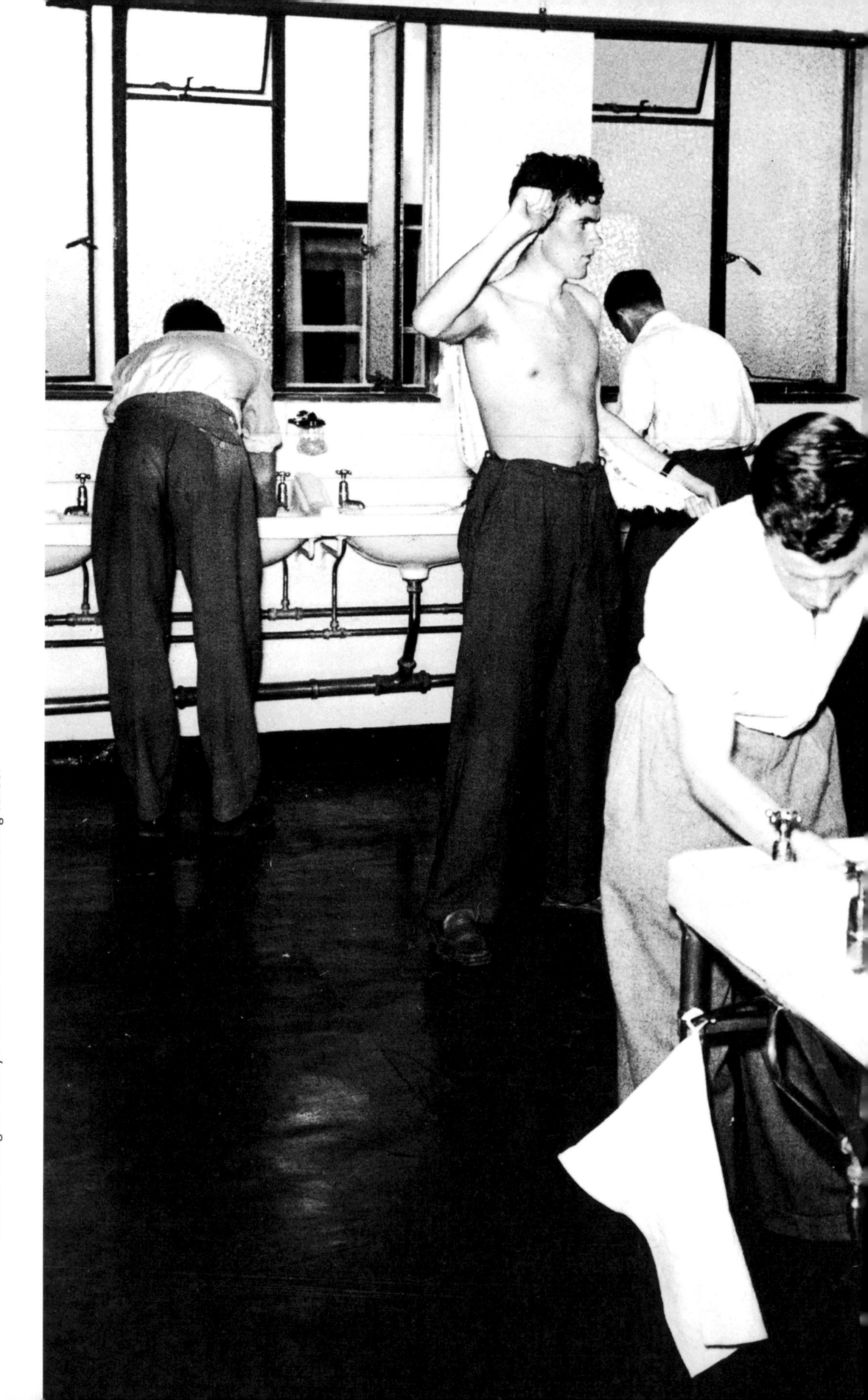

Students waking for the day's tuition at the Porthcurno Training School

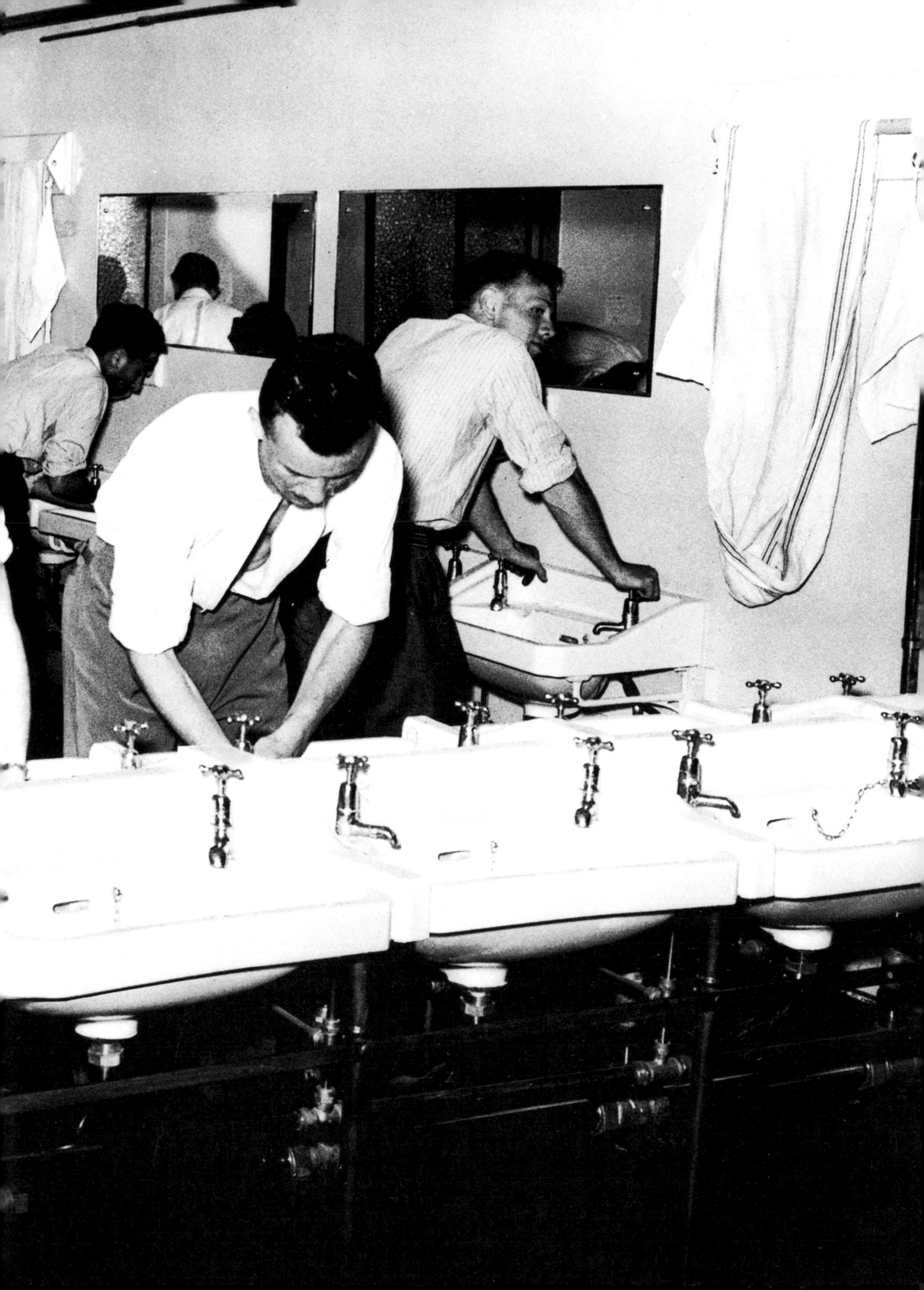

home, coming to Britain. I am of Scottish descent. There was a very large Scottish community in Buenos Aires, in those days it must have been five, six, seven thousand in the city itself. It was almost unheard of anyone within the Scottish community marrying outside the Scottish community. That's all changed now, of course ...

What was the initial appeal of the Company? An interesting question ... To get out and see the world. But not entirely that. In the process of the interview, I was taken up to see the instrument room. And I thought it was the closest thing to magic I had ever seen. I thought, This is going to be *fun* ...

Gustavo Coll *is a Uruguayan national. When Cable & Wireless left Montevideo he acquired the business that he had worked in for the previous twenty years.*

There was an ad in a newspaper [in Montevideo] for two persons to be examined and eventually to be sent abroad. I answered that ad and I was lucky enough to be chosen along with another person for training. That was in 1956, and for some reason or other the other person resigned so only I went to Porthcurno. I was there part of 1957, most of 1958, up to the last days of December. And then I came back as a technician ...

My very first trip abroad was to England. It was a whole new world; and of course a whole new culture, completely different ... I arrived, by boat of course in those days, went to spend the night in a hotel in London, and then by train to Penzance. I still remember it was the 9.30 Cornish Riviera express from Paddington to Penzance and I was amazed at how green the country was, how nice people were to me on board the train. It was nothing like 'stuffy English people', it was nothing of the sort ... It was exciting, it was baffling. I remember sitting on the bus Saturday mornings to take me to Penzance and listening but not understanding the 'natives', because I could never make head or tail of what they used to say among themselves.

Tony Dunne *lives in his native Devon, and joined Cable & Wireless in 1956. The romantic story of his marriage to a Mauritian wife is told below,* *pp 71–2.*

I wanted to be a vet, but when I was sixteen somebody came down to Plymouth College and gave us a demonstration of double-barrelled Morse key and talked about palm trees and grass skirts. And they only wanted five O-levels – I had eight ...

I went to London to Electra House on the Embankment. And I was rather lucky. I was trotting along in my little school cap and my blazer, and I wasn't too sure where Electra House was. I saw some respectable-looking gent plodding along so I doffed my cap and said, 'Excuse me, sir. Can you tell me where to find Electra House?' He said, 'Follow me, boy.' So I followed just behind him, and half-an-hour later found he was my first interviewer. All he wanted to know was if Mr So-and-so was still headmaster at Plymouth College. I said, 'No, he died last term. It's now Mr Dufton, the second master, who's taken over.' 'Oh,' he said, pulled out his little book of the public schools of England, crossed out Bloggs and put in Dufton. 'Good work, boy. That's all.' And that was the first of my three interviews, all of which went on similarly searching lines. Other people I've spoken to apparently got all sorts of grillings. I knew my headmaster was dead, I was thus passed.

I suppose, if my vintage at Cable & Wireless had anything at all in common with each other and it doesn't sound too immodest, they all seemed pleasant, ordinary sort of people. Not in any way academically outstanding. Most of us, not me but most of us, were fairly sporty. I really don't know what they were looking for except possibly people who would fit in well in a mess without raising too many waves.

I was about seventeen and a half when they took me on. We had four terms at Porthcurno, then I went to Nairobi just before my nineteenth birthday. Fortunately the Suez Crisis was on at the time so instead of a three-week trip through the Med to Mombasa I had a six-week trip round the Cape. And of course you get your foreign allowances the day you leave England. Duty-free prices on the boat. We had a ball.

Brian Pemberton *retired from Cable & Wireless in 1993, having been recognised from early in his career as particularly skilled in promoting new types of business. He became a member of the Board in 1983.*

I joined in 1957. The reason that I joined Cable & Wireless was the simple one that I wanted to travel. They put an ad out which basically said: *A Career Abroad?* There was a picture of a rather nice exotic island. The indications were obvious: that you could travel at their expense ...

As a telecoms engineering course, [Porthcurno] was probably the best technical and theoretical telecoms course in the world. It was a fairly remote location. We were much sought after by the lasses of St Levan and Penzance, and you will find a lot of wives in the Company who hail from that part of Cornwall. At Porthcurno, I couldn't afford a car, so I was normally a passenger in one of them which was rather crudely called the *Fornicatorium*, but it was an old Ford actually. They were quite strict at the College. You had your weekends to yourself, but during the week it wasn't really encouraged that you went in to St Just or Penzance. They wanted you really to keep your heads down, so it was only for the hottest of liaisons that you'd see people sneaking out on a Wednesday or something.

I think any of the people you talk to who've gone through Porthcurno, saw it as a terrific bonding exercise, and it gave you all the technical and operational knowledge so you could run a station in a remote location. The rationale from corporate headquarters in Mercury House was to get people together, and during my time there – although it was very nicely done – a couple of people were weeded out who weren't going to be able to cope with, say, the isolation of the Cocos Islands. I made friendships there that endure to this day ... When you get together it's as if the intervening years had just fallen away.

John Worrall *was to become the last Principal of the Cable & Wireless College at Porthcurno before its move to Coventry. He had already been keen on radio before joining the Company in 1957; the travel was an added bonus.*

As I later realised, joining Cable & Wireless was like joining the Services and it was very much how you approached life which determined how well you'd get on ... Part of the training at Porthcurno was living in a mess, rather like a Service mess, and you learned as part of your training not just the technicalities but how to live in a group like that. How to elect a mess president, and to have someone looking after the bar, someone else looking after the sports and social events.

When it came to the end of the training there was another option. The submarine cable apprentices were generally sent into the Tunnels [the cable station there, excavated from the rock during the war] as a working telegraph station for about six months to consolidate their training, which was a useful operation. They could actually get experience on live telegraph equipment and a live circuit without going overseas and blowing a whole station up on their first tour. But we radio students didn't have that option. So we left a little earlier, after about eighteen months' training, and were sent off to exotic spots like Barbados and Nairobi.

I was duly posted to Nairobi, in Kenya, and I was really looking forward to this. I was home on leave before embarkation and got a phone call from Head Office saying, 'Sorry, we're sending you to Cyprus.' This was 1958, and in Cyprus they were having certain problems. EOKA [guerillas fighting for independence from Britain] were running around shooting everybody in sight, including civilians. It turned out that the person from my group that they had posted to Cyprus had just married, and his wife strongly objected to spending her honeymoon effectively under quarantine. I was a bachelor and presumably expendable, and they swapped me and sent him to Nairobi instead. As it turned out, Cyprus was a very pleasant place.

John Bragg *comes from Dorset, and has spent most of his working life in the Far East. He moved to Australia, and now works for Cable & Wireless Optus in Sydney.*

I was at Wellington School and I read in the reference library that Cable & Wireless paid while training, and when you're 15 that's quite interesting ... It wasn't until getting on board the ship in Tilbury Docks in London, I suddenly realised, 'Hey, I'm going off. Where is Zanzibar at any rate?'

Brian Woods *is the youngest member of the small expatriate group of former Cable & Wireless men living in La Paz. He left the Company in mid-career and subsequently worked for the United Nations and the Crown Agents. He has a distinguished record in cataloguing (and discovering new varieties of) the fish and birds of Bolivia.*

I've always been very interested in wildlife. All my books are bird books, my hobbies are bird-watching and breeding fish and writing articles about them. My intention was always to be a zoologist. However, I was convinced, whether correctly or not, that there wasn't very much of a career in zoology. A chap at school had a relation who worked on one of the cable ships, and he had a copy of the Company's then promotional brochure, *Your Career Abroad* – a little blue book ... I wanted to get out of England, to where all the animals and birds and elephants and everything lived. And this was always my theme. I always wanted to get out of England. So really what Cable & Wireless offered me was exactly what I was looking for.

I had an interview, I was accepted, I went to Porthcurno. We're in the early 1960s here. Even going to Cornwall was great because it is the part of England I most like. I come from Dulwich Village in London, but I was always cycling all over the place in Europe. Going to Cornwall was just like a free gift.

Patricia Bosdet, *the second woman to become Chief Clerk of Cable & Wireless, and the first lady Official, was involved thereafter in many new overseas ventures and in the Company's privatisation in 1981. She joined the Head Office staff in 1963.*

I decided I wanted to be a certified accountant, which is one where you train in industry ... It was only when I [went] for the interview, that I found out it was [a] telecommunications company, and even when I got there I think it took me a long time to understand what the Company did. Working in London – at the time there were no UK operations – and as I was quite young and junior, I became a bit detached from what was happening overseas, from what was the coal face of the Company's business. So it took probably three to five years before I really understood what the Company was doing. As you become more senior you realise what is happening; before, you'd understand it in theory, but it didn't really mean anything.

I started working on the ships section. I was in the Finance Department. The overseas locations sent in what in those days were called cash statements, which were just a record of their payments each month. [These] came in from all over the world: South American branches, Spanish branches, Hong Kong, the West Indies, everybody sent in a cash statement. Each of the ships that we had then sent in a cash statement which included all their cash transactions, and also we seemed to have information concerning payments which were deducted out of salaries for personnel on the boats. So you tended to know how much each chap was sending home to his wife, and also assisted money to go into schooling, things like that. You knew how many kids they had. You got to know quite a bit about their lives.

The working style then all just seemed 'normal'. Looking back now, I'm not sure. One of the interesting things: everyone said, 'It is a family firm,' and certainly I think the training in those days made you feel very much part of the firm, the business. That is something that was probably common to a lot of businesses where staff stayed for a long time. Now there is a real change.

Richard Selby *began his training at Porthcurno in September 1966. Now he is in charge of development at the new Cable & Wireless College in Coventry, a wholly different place from the old school in Cornwall.*

It's definitely a bonding process, there are still people I am in touch with even now, 32 years later. And it was all very exciting as you got towards the end of the course: you were all wondering who was going to go where. The course finished in March, I suppose I would have known at the end of January where I was going. Bermuda.

CHAPTER TWO

The way it was – Life at the cable stations

The soul of Cable & Wireless is not just the uniformity, not just the camaraderie. That's part *of its soul – a way of working, this intuitive understanding of what people are doing, the grapevine of people who have a common background, a common understanding. The texture is then supplied by all the local people.*

Peter Moulson

The success of Cable & Wireless was built upon the network of submarine telegraph cables that criss-crossed the globe. That success lasted through the 1940s and 1950s. The last of the old telegraph cables went out of use in 1970, more than a century after the first cables had been laid. By then they had been superseded by other forms of telecommunication – new telephone cables, radio and satellite. Since the 1920s cables and radio have been the backbone of the Company, and the pendulum of the relative importance of the two has swung backwards and forwards over the course of time.

The old system that Cable & Wireless operated was underpinned by a global network of cable stations, and a corresponding web of companies, the Eastern Telegraph Company and the Western Telegraph Company being the most prominent. It had been since 1929 a privately owned but publicly supervised entity that provided the imperial international and commercial message service. Taken into public ownership in 1947, for the world at large this was to become the forgotten giant of telecommunications.

Words like 'patriarchal' and 'hierarchical' recur when the old Cable & Wireless is being discussed. Terminology was often borrowed from the armed forces – messes, postings, tours, leave or furlough – and many of the Company traditions were shared with the Services and other arms of Britain's colonial enterprise. Most who joined the Company expected to spend their working lives within it, and were fiercely proud of their achievements. Many – but certainly not all – who worked overseas and were known as F1 (Foreign Service staff, class 1) led a quasi-colonial, expatriate life. They often suffered considerable privations in many of the out-of-the-way and economically backward locations in which they were expected to work.

Change in the Company was slow to happen, especially technological change. Some found the pace of change painfully slow. Cable & Wireless had a niche market and served that market well, yet it and its employees often discovered that the world they had known was fast disappearing.

John Rippengal, *who joined Cable & Wireless in the early years of the Second World War, here reflects on the ethos of the Company and the expatriate life he led. Although Britain has a long tradition of company personnel working and living overseas, the expatriate lifestyle is to many at home an unknown quantity.*

One of the things that coloured the whole way the Company operated, and its culture, was its in-house training. They didn't take people from outside. This had, in one sense, a tremendous advantage in the sense that they knitted together a group of people who tended to think and operate and rely on each other, so there was a tremendous *esprit* built up. This was for foreign service staff. Home service staff were taken on and had on the job training and that sort of thing, but the foreign service staff were really quite 'elite'. The disadvantage, of course, was that it made it all even more inward-looking ... You were inculcated with a mindset which the old cable entrepreneurs had already produced. They had this idea it was going to go on as it was forever, with the submarine cable network ...

Throughout my career I've found that people don't want to know anything about you being overseas. They just are not interested, and a gap opens up. You become culturally different from people who live [in the UK]. Your mode of existence is different, you entertain much more when you're overseas, you have different interests because you've been to different places ... In those days, by and large, people just couldn't believe you were going round to all these exotic places, one after another, doing sorts of things quite unheard-of here.

Howard Kleyn, *who joined Cable & Wireless in 1950 following National Service, looks back at his life abroad in the Company with an analytical eye.*

The General Examination [taken by staff part-way through their career overseas] was one that prepared you for management. It asked questions like, 'How do you keep the accounts?', and asked you to write a letter to an irate customer, all those sort of things. 'Give the *raison d'être* for cocktail parties in tropical stations' – and there is one, believe it or not. You have to bind yourself into the local community. If you're going to be a telecoms carrier, like in many other businesses, it's no good trying to distance yourself from the customer, you've got to be right next to the customer ... When the customer takes your service you begin, and it is what you do with that customer thereafter which keeps him, and satisfies him or not, as the case may be ... First of all your company must have a good name locally, and that is achieved through these cocktail parties and other social activities. Then you must have your own integrity, which is why slick salesmen never, never sell telecoms.

Basil Leighton, *who spent the final ten years of his time with the Company in Bahrain, until 1981, had previously seen service in almost every part of the world as an engineer and subsequently as a manager. His career straddled the old ways and the changes of the 1970s.*

My strongest memories of Cable & Wireless relate to the submarine cable, the old cable that went under the sea. In those days it was almost like a religion, the submarine cable technology ...

It was cradle to grave, the Company. You were there for life. When you went to a place overseas, somebody met you off the ship, or at the bottom of the runway, and took you through. Somebody helped with your visa, you had a house waiting, which may need furnishing, or you went into a mess. You had a basic set of rules, the F1 rules and regulations: 'Overseas staff are reminded of the necessity of daily evacuation of the bowels,' and 'Juniors are reminded of the dangers of loose living, in the event of any trouble consult the Company's Medical Officer.' These were written down as part of the rules. If your mess bill, which included the drinks you signed for, went above a certain figure you were called to see the Assistant Manager and explain why your bill was high – although his was probably twice as high. You were cocooned into this great Eastern Telegraph, and Eastern Telegraph paid everything. They even paid your tax when you came back to England, that was part of your concessions. You didn't expect to become terribly rich, but you knew you were taken care of, you had a pension at the end of the time. It couldn't apply nowadays, but it did work. You joined, and you were second to the Foreign Office (who had their diplomatic status) in some places, or you were nearly level to some of the banks in other places.

George Warwick *continues the reflective theme with the notion of 'family', something that most older staff and their own families associate with Cable & Wireless and that he encountered first when he was posted to Bermuda in 1945.*

When I joined Cable & Wireless and went overseas for the first time, even though you didn't know anybody there, there was always someone to help you. It was just like going into a family, you soon got to know people, and people stayed together. You had all the strains – some people liked others, some didn't like them – you had all the problems you have in a family, but you stuck together. Wherever you went after that, you nearly always found somebody you'd been on a station with before. Even if you didn't, the people that were there brought you into the community from the moment you landed.

You had a job for life unless you fell over drunk on the manager's mat three times.

The telegraph instrument room at Accra in the mid-1940s

LIFE OVER THE HORIZON

The Cable & Wireless companies operated – and in very many cases continue to operate – in locations scattered around the world. Some in metropolitan cities, some on remote islands. Cable stations, radio stations. Places suitable for wives and families to live in, and places suited mainly to young bachelors prepared to rough it. Until recent years transfers between branches were frequent, and individuals usually have a lengthy list of places both exotic and mundane in which they worked and made a life. For most of them, the contrast with life at home was total, and although some employees had had other members of the family in the Company (and in some cases had themselves been born and brought up overseas), the shock could be as great as the delight.

Ted Amor *spent a substantial part of his early career in Egypt in the late 1940s, on the stations that had been the backbone of the old Eastern Telegraph Company.*

Ever feel homesick? No, no. Boarding school boy. You start off that way ... There wasn't much going on at Suez, but [the mess] was more or less the centre for the small English community that was there. Bankers, canal pilots, people like that. Suez mess was quite a centre of entertainment. We had real parties there.

Tennis and pink gins? Sum it up that way, if you like ...

The office: well, it was rather a mish-mash. The [submarine cables] through to the East and Far East, London–Bombay, London–Singapore, London–Hong Kong and God knows where, all went through there, down to Port Sudan. That side of it was up-to-date 'regenerator' equipment. But the back-up stuff was out of the Victorian era: old gas engines with huge 4 feet, 5 feet flywheels, hot bulb starter, tray Daniel batteries – horrible damn things. A zinc tray and a mixture of sulphuric acid and copper sulphate, a copper slab on top of the anode, and then one piled on top of the other. Terrible stuff. Yet it all worked. It wasn't until 1952 that they were replaced, and they'd been carrying on, oh, fifty or sixty years.

The size of the establishment in Suez: manager, engineer, deputy engineer and four watchkeepers, plus two workshop mechanicians and workshop staff. Battery men, engine men, gardener – there was a little garden in the centre. Operators – two operators on each watch so there'd be about ten operators. Accountant, accounts clerk – local staff. The main staff manager, engineer, deputy engineer and four watchkeepers were F1, foreign service staff. A medium-sized station in fact. Most of the stations chuntered along on a thing that size.

Now, Alexandria was a big station ... London–Alexandria Cable Number 4 was the lifeblood of the old Eastern. It was a high-speed circuit, busy twenty-four hours a day, mainly cotton exchange traffic ... We had a Cotton Exchange Alex–Cotton Exchange Liverpool circuit during the day. You'd see people at the counter – it was all handed in by scribbles, they didn't have their own teleprinters in those days – and somebody would put a quote in in Alex, you'd scribble it down, operator would punch it, put it into the transmitter direct straight through to Liverpool. And within a minute you'd be getting a reply. People were hanging over the circuits waiting for them, and this circuit was put straight through for that reason. You'd get buy and sell exchanges within the minute.

Wendy Suart *arrived in North Borneo from her native Australia in 1949, and soon met her future husband Brian there. He was building a new station in Jesselton after the war.*

Brian had been sent out as an engineer to supervise the building of this new station. At the time of his arrival there was a town office which was a palm-leafed, thatched building, the same as all the buildings in Jesselton, which had been flattened in the war at the end of the Japanese occupation. So the Manager sat in the town office. Down at a beach six miles away there was a wooden hut in which were a few Chinese employees and George Pope,

Feluccas on the River Nile, one of Ted Amor's snapshots
from his time spent in Egypt

Caught napping on duty in Alexandria

the mechanician. He was in charge of digging trenches, laying land lines and all that sort of thing.

When Brian arrived, the work really started. He had to clear 72 acres of land. Legend has it that it was chosen by two men in an aeroplane flying above it – the Singapore manager and somebody else – and they looked down and said, 'Ah, that looks like a nice flat stretch, we'll buy that.' Well, swamps usually *are* flat ... Once the water was drained out to the sea, Brian then had to survey it and put up his masts and string his aerials. Then supervise contractors building a large office with instrument room, engine room, boiler room, with quarters for the coolies and a house for their foreman, a house for the manager and a house for the engineer (which was us) and a house for the bachelors' mess. There was a great deal of work on the drawing board, and it took him the three years he was there.

There was a weekend when a cable ship laid the 'shore end' [of the cable] into Jesselton from Hong Kong. To this wooden building on the beach. All around the walls were desks pushed to the walls where the Chinese men were working, and in the middle of this cleared space was the boat which Brian was building. In the background, through a hole in the wall, you could see the Hong Kong cable coming in as a loop; having emerged from the South China Sea and across the foreshore it comes through the wall of this hut. This little loop of cable to me summed up the whole essence of Jesselton. Work was pushed to the margins and the most important thing – the boat building – went on in the middle of the floor.

George Warwick *had a house by the beach in Ngombo, Ceylon, close to the wireless station, when he was stationed there in the early 1950s, that was far from being an idyll. The standards of accommodation could vary drastically from one posting to another.*

A cottage, brick-built, belonged to a fisherman, there wasn't much to it: a lean-to kitchen, a stove the company provided. It didn't have a proper bathroom – a sandbox for a toilet and our bath was one of those tin tubs. It didn't seem to matter. We didn't have to pull the water from the well ourselves,

Boat building seemed to take precedence at Jesselton.
The end of the cable pokes through the slats of the right-hand wall.

someone else did that. From there, we moved into an old plantation bungalow which was high and quite big. Not a lot of rooms, but really big and cool, and designed so that air flowed through it. You had to have mosquito nets. The disadvantage with that place was that scorpions would come out and skitter round the place at night. You'd get these big lizards, six feet long, in the garden, but they weren't going to attack anybody. We had a snake get up into the room; we were sitting out in the garden and we could see this damned thing waving around. I can tell you, we tucked the mosquito nets in very well after that.

Keith and Pat Warren *found themselves in the same place a short while afterwards. For them, a newly married couple, the privations turned out to be life-threatening.*

We did manage to find a small bungalow on the beach, owned by a fisherman. It was fairly basic, as so many things were out there. There wasn't running water for a start, you had to take water from a well, which the fishermen also used; and the fishermen tended to use the beach as a lavatory and as a depository for dead pigs and things like that.

The result of all this was, I got typhoid.

Pat: It makes you grow up though when you're in a strange country and something like that happens. I think youth is on your side then, because you really don't worry about it in the way perhaps you would when you were more mature.

Richard Histed, *who had joined Cable & Wireless in 1954, was fourth generation with the Company. He had a fair idea of what to expect, but the isolation and the domestic difficulties of his first lengthy posting were both alarming and exciting.*

I went overseas, first of all to Lisbon: the idea was that I learned Portuguese, but everyone spoke English. There was a possibility to learn, but no-one took it seriously. Then I went to Recife for six months, in north Brazil, and then

I went to Belém do Para on the Amazon. I think the town had a population of about 80,000 and there were something like sixteen people who spoke English, so I learned Portuguese very fast. Otherwise you didn't speak to anybody.

We wore white linen suits. You had two, and each suit had two pairs of trousers. You would walk to the office, because we didn't have any other means of transportation, and you'd get wet, no air-conditioning, absolutely soaked in perspiration. When you got in you'd hang your jacket up, and since we were on the engineering side we had a change of clothes at the office to change into. When you came home at the end of your shift, you put your jacket back on and came home. When you got home you had a shower – if there was water. We didn't have gas, we had electricity which came on about 2 o'clock in the morning to about 4 o'clock in the morning, which wasn't much use. We had these pressurised hurricane lamps, rather like a primus with a filament over it, and they were absolutely brilliant. They had a heat equivalent to a 1000-watt bulb – the light was equivalent to a 1000-watt bulb, but the amount of heat they put out was absolutely enormous. When you're sitting in a room with a temperature of about 84, and the humidity about 96, the last thing you want is a 1000-watt fire blaring at you. That was it, otherwise you sat in the dark.

There was a Manager and two of us expats, I suppose there were about forty people. We were right at the end of the line, we were somewhere in the region of 300 or 400 miles up the Amazon. Above that the sand banks used to shift so much that any cables got broken. We were the [cable system's] northernmost point in Brazil. We had land lines from our cable hut where the submarine cables came in about 6 to 7 kilometres in length, and they went through a swamp. On one occasion they broke, and we had nearly a kilometre of cable which was lost forever. How far down it had gone in the swamp one will never know. You couldn't have land lines in the Amazon, because the territory there is very sodden ground, all covered in swamps, and the Amazon floods something like sixty miles either side of its banks in the rainy season (which is not when it rains, but when the snow melts in the Andes between two and three thousand miles away).

Ian Corrall *a short time later found himself in Bahrain. He had only radio experience (a more common phenomenon by the early 1960s than it had been before). The young Corrall was thrown in at the deep end.*

After about three or four weeks, I was left in charge of one of the larger telegraph offices in the Company. We worked all the places round the Gulf, to London and what have you, but I was well supported. I had six local staff, technicians: Indians, Pakistanis, Anglo-Indians, and a Lebanese teleprinter mechanic. We had Bahraini operators and counter staff. I had quite a hairy first six months, but Brian Suart [the Manager] was very helpful to me. I got the usual chat – oh, you know, they said, 'About three months and we'll have somebody else to take over, you'll see.' Well, of course, you're as green as grass at the age of 21 and on your first tour, so you believe them. In fact, it's the oldest trick in the book the Company use: they shove you in deeper, and if you swim they leave you, but, OK, if you make a bit of a mess they pull you out, no hard feelings, and they get somebody else. Apparently I survived ...

Water. The drinking water was delivered by donkey cart, and you had to pay a rupee a gallon for it. The tap water was brackish. You could drink it, in fact the Company's doctor – Doc Snow, must have been in his 70s – reckoned that you should drink it, because the salts in it were all good for you and so forth. But the trouble was that until you got used to it you were rocket propelled for about a week. It just went straight through. I hardly drank it. We used to take these salts. Those were the days when they were always on about taking these salt tablets. It's interesting that the clothing lists – the ones I first got when I arrived there – still had spine protectors, because the sun would make your spine brittle. I don't think you could have bought them then, but it was on the list. These things just carried on. And topees. You never saw anyone wearing a topee.

Basil Leighton *spent a very considerable part of his career in Bahrain. The first time, as a younger man in the mid-1950s, he was wary of its charms, as he describes here. On his return some fifteen years later he was to find it an interesting and challenging place to live and work.*

Cable & Wireless, I have to say, were a bit slow in providing such facilities as air-conditioning. Other firms had perhaps gone ahead with it; eventually Cable & Wireless provided it, but being a British company they decided to find their air-conditioners in the UK. Well, regrettably the UK hadn't had much experience, not like the Americans or the Japanese who had a lot of experience, so they decided to send us Biddle units, made by a firm called Biddle, who tested them out in Hampshire, and they seemed to work there. And to save money, we as engineers at the branch were supposed to maintain them. Whereas an American unit would be about [a yard across], Biddle units were like an organ. They occupied half the room, they clanked away, and you got a bit of cool air out of them, which was hardly effectual. I was lucky: we lived in the mess and decided to replace the curtains, and I was able to get hold of the old curtains. I made a tent within the large bedroom which I put over the Biddle unit, put my bed within the tent inside the room, and by that means the amount of cooling you got was increased. Still not very good, but better than we had before. Prior to the Biddle units we slept up on the roof of the mess – this is July, August, September, when it was so hot, so humid – and even there, you had to get up two or three times in the night to take a shower. We slept up there with just a wooden canopy over us to reduce the dew.

Chris Schofield, *whose first Company posting had been to the busy station of Alexandria, discovered the charm and the difficulty of maintaining a far-flung telecommunications empire when he was sent in 1959 to one of the remotest of all its outposts, in the Pacific halfway between Fiji and Hawaii.*

Very rashly towards the end of my tour [lecturing at Porthcurno] I asked for more money. My feet never touched the ground from that moment. They told me they were posting me to Fanning Island. I went round asking people, 'Where is Fanning?' Nobody knew. Had anybody ever been there? Nobody knew of anyone who had been there. My wife got a bit worried because we'd just had a son, who was about nine months old, a year at the most, and we were going to Fanning Island. If anybody had gone there they hadn't come back as far as we could see, so we were a bit apprehensive.

In those days it was all boats. We got on to the *Strathmore* and sailed down very leisurely. We were off Perth. We had this small baby, in nappies, we were down in H deck or something, it was hot and we were in a heck of a state. A tap on the cabin door. I opened the door, and this charming lady in long white gloves, picture hat, dress was outside. 'You are the Schofields? Yes, well, I'm the Manager's wife from Perth, just thought I'd come and see how you were getting on?' We were really in a stew. 'And there's one thing I have to ask you: what food do we order for you for the next six months? Because you *are* aware that on Fanning, you only get a ship every six months and therefore you must put in an order?' ...

We flew out of Sydney ... Then they had a little island-hopping plane, six passengers and a wing and a prayer. It came back to Suva [in Fiji] and we met the Manager there. We were shown *John Williams III*, which was owned by the London Missionary Society. It was a tiny little ship, I suppose 200 tons or something. It really was made for missionaries, the bunks were about 4 feet 6 inches long, it was incredibly cramped. No air-conditioning system as such – there was an air blower, and the first mate used an appalling hair pomade, which circulated all round the ship. Four or five days' voyage. Then the skipper said, 'Go out on the deck and look for green clouds.' Sure enough, we spotted them ... The palm trees reflected up, because Fanning Island at the most is about four feet above the water mark, and the palm trees possibly twenty, thirty feet above that, so there's not a lot to look for. And missionary ships weren't equipped with radar or anything else. This was 1959.

Because it was a small community – there were twelve families there – it was essential to keep them busy and to avoid any introspection or anything else. So we led a really hectic social life, but it was more or less essential because the people who did get introspective, really went round the ... The other snag was that with the infrequency of the boats one didn't build up any resistance, so when people came in with common colds, we all went down with them.

Maurice Bane, *like many of his wartime generation of recruits, was posted to a succession of the North Africa, Red Sea and Mediterranean posts of the old-style Eastern Telegraph Company. Many of these stations were to be closed in the course of the 1950s amid the political upheaval of that era. The camaraderie and the numbers of people involved were a far cry from the Fanning Islands of the Cable & Wireless system.*

When I got to Port Sudan, there were seven bachelors in the mess, and the Engineer and the Manager, and we all lived [at the station]. The office was at the bottom of the garden, with tennis courts in between, so you would wander from the mess down the garden. Yes, life was pretty good there. There was the Red Sea Club, the Hotel, the desert stretched right away and you could see the Red Sea hills in the distance. Glorious sunsets. We went up into the hills ... for a break. You needed a break because it was so hot there, to cool off. If we were on night duty and wanted to sleep in the afternoon, we used to sprinkle our beds with water and then switch the overhead fan on and the evaporation would cool us off. It was pretty hot there in the summer when the sun was up, but everybody took it in their stride. We swam, drank, played tennis. There's not a lot I can say about Port Sudan except life went along.

John Howie, *another wartime recruit to Cable & Wireless who spent his formative years with the Company in North Africa and the Mediterranean, found that travelling to Port Sudan was quite as interesting as anything he actually did at the station itself.*

I transferred to Port Sudan. At Port Said I was supposed to connect with the *Taif* of the Khedivial Mail Line ... When I heard the *Taif* had lost its propeller in Aden, I asked the Manager there to ask Head Office if I could go overland, as I had always wanted to travel the Nile. Head Office agreed, so I caught the night express to Aswan from Cairo. From Aswan by paddle steamer to Wadi Halfa, first class. I had the top deck with wonderful vistas of the stars at night. (Second class was the main deck with the engines, and third class was a barge tied alongside shared with a few cows, pigs, etc.) The steamer tied up at Abu Simbel so we could visit the wonderful temple of Ramses II, later cut into pieces and moved uphill when the Aswan Dam was built. Wadi Halfa, on the border of the Sudan, to Port Sudan was another train, across the Nubian Desert, for two days. The attendant came round occasionally with a feather duster to clear all the sand which infiltrated the windows, and the passengers.

On the night express to Aswan on his way to Port Sudan, John Howie had met a doctor going back home to the super-wealthy Abud Pasha's sugar estate.

Much later, in Suez, I became due for some local leave, so I wrote to this Coptic doctor, with whom I had kept up a correspondence, and was invited to visit. Again the night express to Aswan, but this time I was instructed to tell the driver to stop at a station they never stopped at. In the morning, the attendant woke me to say we were entering Abud Pasha's estates. When I rushed to get dressed, he smiled and said we would not arrive at the station for another two hours! I gazed out of the window at sugar cane to the horizon, and eventually the train stopped and I got out, watched by all the curious passengers. A smartly uniformed Egyptian asked my name and indicated a large Rolls Royce, which drove half a mile down to the river bank where an immaculate motor launch and crew lay.

We set off up the river, rocking the slowly moving dhows, and after half an hour arrived at a jetty on the opposite bank where my doctor friend from the train was waiting with his charming wife. After a clean-up we went to meet Abud Pasha, a very pleasant man, married to an English lady ... I visited all there was to see in Thebes, and in the evenings I sat with my friends in the gardens on the river bank, chewing chilled sugar cane, with a drink, and watching the timeless Nile glide by with its cargo of dhows.

Maurice Bane *discovered the hard way that West Africa was still a dangerous place for an expatriate's health. The usual retirement age from the Company was 55, another indication that employees had often had hard and debilitating lives in out-of-the-way stations.*

Accra, I think I did two years. You were only supposed to do 18 months because of malaria and blackwater fever. I had malaria a couple of times, but fortunately ... It occasionally comes back, but it's nothing significant really.

Basil Leighton *puts it more succinctly.*

It was either the climate or the gin that got you in the old days.

Howard Kleyn *had forewarning of what life might be like on one of the more deprived and self-enclosed postings that Cable & Wireless possessed. At that time, the early 1950s, Cable & Wireless still had a Company station in Pakistan.*

One day a chap of more or less my own age came through Karachi from Muscat going home on leave. He had had a very serious bout of prickly heat. It's all to do with the salt on the skin and the fact that you're under the tropical sun all the time. When he came into Karachi I went down to the ship to meet him. 'Come on, we'll go and have a spot of lunch in the Boat Club.' When we got there, he got out of the car and fell down on the lawn. He said, 'Grass, grass, green grass.' When I was later posted to Muscat myself, I viewed it with considerable trepidation remembering the state of mind of this man who'd emerged from a year there.

John Davenport *had been posted to the Arabian Gulf territory of Muscat not long thereafter, as something of a punishment for playing football with local boys. His experiences seem much more extreme than might be expected from barely more than forty years ago.*

Muscat was a remarkable place. It was in the days of the old Sultan ... It was probably a hundred years behind everywhere else. There were no paved roads, for example. It was a walled city. They fired the gun at sunset, closed the gates and after that if you were caught out without your little hurricane lamp, which we called 'butties', they'd shoot you. So if you were called down to the office in the evening because something had gone wrong, you lit your paraffin lamp and hoped that it wouldn't go out on the way down to the office. The soldiers used to go round in pairs with loaded rifles and they had orders to shoot anybody who didn't have his little lamp with him, the basis being if you had a lamp you obviously weren't up to no good. If you didn't have a lamp you clearly were up to no good, you see, so you were fair game. And we couldn't travel very far. We could go to Muttra but we couldn't go beyond Muttra – well,

The Company's staff at Accra in May 1948

we were allowed to go to the sultan's beach, which was across uncharted desert really, but we couldn't go any further than that without getting a pass.

The Manager and his wife lived in a very large old Arab house with a central courtyard and a verandah all the way round. We three bachelors lived in another Arab house which was the mess. Very limited modern conveniences: we had chemical toilets, we bathed in a tin bath on the verandah. In the summer a great new innovation just after I got there was the introduction of air-conditioning – but the company would only air-condition one bedroom, so in the summer we all moved into one air-conditioned bedroom, all three of us. Liquor was rationed. We used to barter it ...

You have to bear in mind the European community in Muscat numbered probably about twelve, and that included the American mission people, so it was a pretty small community. After eighteen months, you were beginning to go a bit gaga. Definitely.

Colin Sharp *had also been based in Muscat early in his career, around 1950. His next posting, after this calamity, was in Montevideo, and most of his subsequent career was to be spent in Spanish-speaking South America.*

Muscat was totally isolated, it had a ship once every two weeks. There was no fresh food, you lived practically on pills; we had occasional camel, which was brought in as meat. Sometimes we'd get potatoes off the ships. The diet was terrible, and the Company made no effort to do anything about the service length there. It was extraordinary that nobody understood what the conditions of life were. Of course, in Muscat, there was no air-conditioning. I've seen it go to 117°F at midnight. The wind would come off the desert, it would just go soaring up. I had a large *Bartholomew's Atlas*, the backs of the atlas would curve and practically meet it was so dry. Yet that was when the Company treated the F1 very much as they always had: that you had to go anywhere and you had to get on with it. We were only five white people in Muscat ... I was not there a long time, yet I caught typhoid.

Ian Corrall *was to spend many years in and out of the various states in the Gulf and the Middle East. He was on his way to his first proper posting, in Bahrain (see above, p. 47), after his time spent 'consolidating'.*

It was 1958. We went up the Gulf, dropping stuff off, various places. I think Muscat was one of the places in those days where they still dressed for dinner. There were only six expats in Muscat, nothing much else, one little old cable that used to go over to Aden. The only reason they were there was that it was part of the agreement with the British Government that Muscat had external communications. I think it was something like ten telegrams a day – no way were they going to make any money out of it.

We stopped off at various places like Bandar Abas. In those days, Bandar Abas was a Muscat enclave on the other side of the Gulf, between Iran and Pakistan. I remember this: absolutely magic, going in in the morning the sea was absolutely glass calm, and there was a fog, a sea mist, and you could just see in the distance. The ship went in with a leadsman on either side of the bow, because there were no maps in those days. They were actually canting the ship in, and dropped anchor. And all these dhows appeared.

Ted Amor *switched out of the traditional life of the old Eastern Telegraph Company, with its large messes and big staffs, into restricted island life in the Atlantic. In the first half of the 1950s he served first on the Cape Verde Islands and then the Azores.*

When you steam into St Vincent [Cape Verde Islands] you steam in from the north approach and all you see is a barren rock. Just sand and rock and nothing. You think, 'Oh my God!' But as you turn the headland, in front of you opens the most magnificent harbour in the world. It's a volcano broken down on a third of its rim. Deep harbour, towering top of the volcano ... And as you come in, you see a little town – it's baking hot by the way – Portuguese-style, red-tiled roofing, busy harbour. Ships were in because it was also a coaling station or a fuelling station. The big companies were Miller & Corey and Shell. And Cable & Wireless. Certainly people didn't look to be very well off, and they *were* poor. And you walked, no transport ... The difficulty was, there was nothing there. Water had to come from another island. We were rationed; we lived there two and a half years, and we lived on five gallons of water a day.

And social life? Can you imagine thirty English people entertaining thirty English people? We put on little shows, tomfoolish little shows where the actors would be the next session's audience. The other thing they had there was an old cine projector, dated about 1905. This had been left by Ernest Shackleton, on the way back from one of his trips to the Antarctic. All his ships used to call in at cable stations ... It had ceased to work so I thought, 'I'll have a go at this.' And I got it going. The arc lamp – you ought to hear the moans from the office generators when I cut the arc in ... There was a local jack-of-all-trades, Tuto Melo, used to do everything – the bloke would fix your car, fix your fridge, fix this, fix that. He had the idea of creating an open-air cinema ... We sold him the projector, I fitted him up a sound head, he bought an anamorphic lens, and he started importing films. And that was the first public cinema in the Cape Verde Islands, on Ernest Shackleton's projector. I remember the first film we saw there was that 1953 production, *War of the Worlds.*

Maurice Bane *speaks for many when he describes the magical natural beauty of aspects of life overseas even in some of the less enticing locations such as Port Sudan.*

You're in a foreign environment, yet the days are very mundane. Often you did the same thing, particularly in your early working days on six-hourly watches, and yet there was always, because you were overseas, that touch of romanticism about it. If you're on night duty, you watch the dawn come up. And glorious dawns they were overseas. You think, life is good. If you were going to go into the mess and have a breakfast of camel meat and beans you didn't mind because life wasn't too bad ...

Panoramic view of St Vincent, Cape Verde Islands

Then it was time to return to England for the first time after five years away.

Up to Paris, then the train to Calais, and then the sight of the White Cliffs of Dover. I must admit I felt a bit emotional, because it had been a long time. Travelling through the French countryside you were back to reality perhaps; the thought was, had we been living in a fool's world for a long, long time?

Richard Selby, *who was recruited in the early 1960s, found as many had before him that a few years' absence abroad made a considerable difference.*

I'd gone away when I was about 20. I must have been 24 when I came back, and yes, I was browner, I had a moustache. They didn't recognise me. My mum, dad and sister didn't recognise me at the airport.

Brenda Histed*'s experience when her expatriate life came to an end in the 1980s, after nearly thirty years abroad with her husband, was a keen reminder of what a wrench a life abroad might be for those who were left behind.*

My family were sad to see me go each time and delighted to see me home, and it was just a way of life. But I didn't realise until we finally came home ... I phoned my sister and I said, 'Oh, Joanie, I'm home. That's it, I'll never have to go off again.' She said, 'Brenda, I'm so pleased. The day I saw your ship sail to Recife I knew what it's like to have a broken heart.' And she never did tell me. She said, 'I saw your ship go away, and I thought, that's my little sister.' And until I came back after all those years, she had never told me – and I thought that was wonderful. We'd write lots of letters but I'd no idea quite how they felt.

CABLE WAYS

For the majority of the overseas expatriate staff, engineers and managers, their reason for existence was the cable station. Tennis, swimming, drinks after sundown (or even before) were supplementary to the demands of the system that needed to be maintained and to be kept running. The cables themselves had to be protected, and breaks repaired as swiftly as possible. The messages needed to be sent to and fro swiftly. The electromechanical equipment that the men had been trained to clean and repair needed to be kept in full working order. This was a way of life that had in so many essentials changed little between the 1880s and the 1950s. Even much of the equipment, in looks and in date, went back to the later years of Victoria's reign.

Maurice Bane, *who spent his early years working for the Company in a number of stations around the Mediterranean and the Red Sea, describes here the round-the-clock routine that was the essence of the larger cable stations.*

We worked round the clock: you'd do 6 to 1 in the evening, the next day 1 to 7 in the afternoon, next day 7 am to 1 pm, and the next day night duty, and we were just really keeping all this wonderful brass and mahogany ticking over. Which in the main it did ... We weren't really dealing in high-level development engineering, we were maintaining what was basically a marvellous system. When you think that the whole thing was governed by a reed, which was controlled by a clock. And across the whole world, east and west, all that system depended on that reed ticking away, controlled so everything was synchronous all the way through. London to Gibraltar, Gibraltar to Malta, Malta to Alex[andria], Alex to Suez, Suez to Port Sudan. Port Sudan to Aden, Aden to Colombo, or Aden to Seychelles. Colombo to Penang, Penang to Singapore ... No wonder we felt a bit pleased with ourselves in some ways.

John Davenport, *as did almost every young engineering recruit until the end of the 1950s, experienced the routine slog of keeping the submarine cable communications system going. This was the scene he observed in Aden.*

There were certain things that went on on a very repetitive basis on a cable system. In order to send messages in both directions at the same time you have to 'balance' the cable, and over a period of time this balance varies. Typically over a period of an hour or so, this balance slowly goes out of balance, and everything stops. All the messages stop. It was called an RBP – a routine balance pause. Everything stops by prior notification. Usually what happened was that the alarm bell would ring, because somebody in either London or Singapore had the responsibility of determining when it was time to do another balance check. The alarm bell would go, you'd scamper over to the circuit, see it was a routine balance pause and then you'd have about two minutes to get your balance back in before [cable] traffic would start up again ... When you consider that we had several cable chains going through Aden, that was keeping you on your toes fairly frequently, and that went on night and day. Then you'd be allocated a number of – we called them instruments, there'd be regenerators and all sorts of things used to regenerate the signals – which we had to maintain. So you'd be doing routine maintenance on some of those every time you were on watch.

Things used to quieten down a bit during the evening. If you can imagine a *large* room, full of instruments and people, this whole place – it was I guess about half-past four in the morning – had gone very quiet, and everybody except me was fast asleep. And I was actually reading a novel . Suddenly I was conscious of somebody standing the other side of the Assistant Engineer's desk. I looked up and it was the Branch Engineer who commanded a great deal of respect in those days, especially for a watchkeeper like me. Before I could say a word he said, 'Pretty fine dormitory you've got here, Davenport.' So I sort of said, 'Yes, yes sir' ... I can only assume that because I was awake he was happy. I think if I'd been asleep and everybody else had been asleep, there would have been all hell to pay.

The clock that governed communications and ruled Cable & Wireless's employees' lives stood in each cable station, as here at Mollendo, Peru

John Packer *is one of the leading lights behind the Museum of Submarine Telegraphy at Porthcurno, preserving the type of equipment that he was once putting to active use. In 1959 he was based on Ascension Island, far away in the South Atlantic.*

It was during the Duke of Edinburgh's world tour. He called at Ascension and all the staff were lined up on the pier to meet him. He asked me what I was doing, as he asked all the others. I wasn't actually on watch in the cable station, I was in the maintenance workshop where we used to have to mend things when they went wrong. So I said, 'I'm connected with the cable station' – which was a pretty silly reply really because almost everyone on the island was connected in some way – and he wittily said, 'Connected by what, by cables?' When he went into the station he said, 'It looks a bit old-fashioned.' I had to agree with him because it was still the teak boxes and polished brass which you see in the museum at Porthcurno, which were all still in use. It was the dying decade of the old-fashioned cable telegraphy. I found it fascinating, not so much from a leading technology point of view but the other: fancy we're still doing it this way. The cables were working. Some of them had been laid there for fifty or sixty years, since the 1890s, and they were still working. Why switch them off? It was earning revenue for the Company, telegrams were passing ...

I was a very junior technician, I just accepted that this was the way submarine cables worked. I now realise with hindsight that it was the dying of the old submarine cables and in were coming these new telephone cables, leading up now to fibre optics. Changes came thick and fast. What I was working on was equipment that had not changed for the last thirty or forty years, and some of the equipment had lasted a hundred years. The testing equipment – the way to test a fault or a break in the cable – had been used back in the 1870s ... I was just in time to see the end of a particular way of life in all these remote islands, and of a particular technology.

A press photograph sent by facsimile of HRH Prince Philip being shown cable gear on Ascension

Ted Amor *worked in very many hot and dusty places around the world.*

There was no air-conditioning in those days. You had to have ventilation because of the heat. And the main trouble in all those tropical stations was dust. Humidity and dust. This is why Cable & Wireless was so long in going over to electronics, because at least you didn't have to bother with such finicky details as temperature and humidity control. If it was electro-mechanical it kept on working whatever, so long as you looked after it.

Pat Cowan *was stationed on the remote Indian Ocean island of Rodrigues, a staging post in a long line of cables, in 1959. He and his colleagues still gazed with awe at what their pioneering predecessors had been able to achieve.*

The cable ship came to do some repairs off the island ... It was doing some of the first cable repair work on the cables into Rodrigues (which went from Mauritius to Rodrigues and then on to Cocos Island and then on to Australia, and in the other direction to South Africa). The South Africa–Australia cable chain. These were some of the first repairs since the cables were laid in the 1890s. The Cocos cable had hardly been touched, that whole cable, it was still working at the same original speed except it was automatic, instead of [retransmission of messages by] hand as when it was originally put in – connecting us back to the Boer War.

Paul Foster, *working in the late 1940s as a telegraph operator in the Caribbean, found there were some places that were still using archaic technology that had been employed on the very earliest cables of the 1860s. Stationed on the island of St Kitts, he encountered the mirror galvanometer.*

I have never forgotten the way they received cable messages from St Croix. Remember in the old days, if you went to get your photograph taken the

Paying out cable for laying underwater from the cable tank

photographer would put a big black thing over his head and you'd be upside down? In the station there was a kind of telephone kiosk, a big cupboard with a black curtain. When they were ready and were going to send a message you would pull your chair in, take the cloth and put it over you. You'd be in complete black but on the piece of paper you were writing on was a little dot of light; when you hit a dot the light went up in the air and when you hit a dash it went down. So you would have your pad there, and [the St Croix end] would send up and down and you would write. That was how we received the messages. It wasn't by ear, it was by sight. I never experienced that anywhere else. It must have been the end of an era there.

John Packer *still takes a philosophical view of the way that the cable stations were run.*

Looking back ... from the standpoint of today we were a bunch of amateurs. It was bodge, make do and mend. But having said that, you can say the same thing if you look at the early technology of any technical subject – the first computers were a mess, a bunch of wires and valves glowing away and the thing would only work for two hours at a time until something blew.

ROMANCE

Young men working abroad for Cable & Wireless were supposed to remain single. Marriage below the age of twenty-five was officially frowned upon – the privileges of married living (travel, accommodation and the like) were not extended to the couple, and there were other, less formal sanctions. For some young men, in remote locations, the opportunities to meet women were limited. In some places, the temptations and the opportunity were rather greater.

Ted Amor *was, and remains, a keen musician and amateur impresario.*

At Alexandria, I bullied this lot from the mess into taking part in *Pirates of Penzance* and spent hours drilling their parts into them, because none of them could read music. Then the lovesick maidens, the female part of the cast, came from the English girls' college. So you can blame me and *Pirates of Penzance* for at least three Eastern Telegraph Company marriages.

Ron Werngren, *who was himself brought up in Buenos Aires, knew at first hand that the system he was to join offered plenty of romantic opportunities.*

Western Telegraph in the 'good old days' in the 1920s and 1930s had a very large British staff, contract staff, mostly young bachelors. So they were very much in demand in the Scottish and English communities in Buenos Aires. That in itself made it, 'Oh yes, The Western Telegraph.' You knew about it. You might not have known much of what it was about, but you knew of its existence. There were the railways, a couple of banks, Western Telegraph, that formed a pool of eligible young bachelors ...

Colin Stubbs *had broken the rules about when he could get married after studying on his advanced course in Porthcurno. 'Marrying below the strength', as the phrase was, could bring penalties.*

The Company sent me to Port Sudan. Now shades of the 'old colonial boys' crept in again. It was a punishment station. They didn't really have wives there. I could have gone to a place where at least they had other women, but Port Sudan was the last stop on the way to hell. Awful place.

I can remember Pat and I dashing up on deck as the ship got into Port Sudan. Dashing up on deck. I was quite pleased, showing my wife what it's like overseas. I got up on deck, looked up and said, 'That can't be it. There's nothing, must be on the other side.' So I went to the other side – and said, 'That can't be right, there's nothing there either'. It was just a few houses and sand. The Manager had a flat in a two-storey block in a single staff mess, beneath it were what could have been large flats, but they were full of furniture in store. They didn't bother to give us one of those, we ended up living in a tin-roofed rest house place next to the Red Sea Club ... That's hardly a way to introduce your wife to the glories of overseas life. The women all left there when the hot season came.

Pat Cowan, *stationed on the remote Indian Ocean island of Rodrigues, met and married the daughter of the Manager there.*

My wedding on Rodrigues was a Company do. The cable ship came from Mauritius and brought the bride's veil and gloves and ring. We were married by the Postmaster officially at 7 o'clock in the morning, on his way to work, because you had to have a civil wedding and then a church wedding. The church wedding in mid-afternoon. We actually had a few more people there because we had the cable ship crew, which we hadn't quite expected. So we had a few more colleagues, and a lot of the local people there. We had to get dispensation for the organist: it was a Roman Catholic island, he was Roman Catholic, so to come and play the organ in the Church of England, St Barnabas, he had to get special dispensation. Then we borrowed the hospital Land Rover to go off on our honeymoon, which was spent in a small tin hut down on the end of the island. There was nowhere else to go. We sent [my parents] a telegram to say we were getting married, and there was not a lot they could do about it ... They met their daughter-in-law two and a half years later, but that was the way that a lot of life was.

Marie-Louise and Tony Dunne *met on Mauritius when he was stationed there in 1960. They encountered the old-fashioned attitudes that still prevailed in many parts of the Company. They now live in Devon, having spent their working and married lives abroad.*

Tony was twenty-one, I was nineteen. Oh, it was just boyfriend-girlfriend thing. I was just having a good time. There was a big cocktail party at some place ... and the next day the manager called him in, said, 'Dunne, I'll have you shipped out to Bahrain.' For getting in a tangle with a girl. Me. So he left. And then I followed three months later.

Tony: The one who threw me out, was an oldish manager. When I got to Bahrain across came Brian Suart, the General Manager, who was then very young for such a post. He said, 'Oh, that seems a bit hard. We've got a spare house.' Any room or anything there cost considerably more than my total salary. 'If you can pay for her to get here you can have this house for ... It'll cost you ten shillings for a refrigerator every month.' And I never did discover what that bit of financial wizardry was, but I was very happy to do it. They held the reception, he gave Marie-Louise away, Wendy Suart went round all the staff there saying, 'You'll give them a frying pan, you'll give them a cup and saucer,' and so on. They couldn't have been nicer.

Marie-Louise: I couldn't cook, you know. So every day Wendy came home and taught me something. Oh, yes. It was marvellous.

Tony: She's still got that little notebook she wrote. How to stew mutton and other Australian delicacies.

John Davenport *was surprised to discover on Zanzibar in the late 1950s that old colonial attitudes were still paramount.*

I went from Gibraltar to Zanzibar, and the only way I could play soccer there was to play with the locals. Unbeknown to me this went down very badly with the station Manager as this was 'fraternising with the natives'. I'm absolutely certain that's why I got nine days' notice to pack my bags and go to Muscat. There were largely unwritten rules about fraternisation, but there were enough stories – well, enough incidents that you were aware of where people had been moved on quickly, especially if they'd become romantically entwined with [local people].

In one particular case in Zanzibar, I remember, I was the junior member of the mess and we'd had a mess party, a dance, and invited the Manager and his wife. We'd also invited the daughters of the Anglo-Indian operators, some of whom were really quite attractive young ladies. And when [the Manager] heard about this he let the Mess President know that this was *not* to happen again; we were not to invite the daughters of the Anglo-Indian operators, this was just not done. Ironically, when the party was over it was my job as a junior member of the mess to escort him and his wife down to their car. And she said to me, 'Oh, Mr Davenport, I have enjoyed myself so much. I do hope you'll invite us to the next party.' But he had made it clear there wasn't to be a next party.

It was that sort of thing which led me to realise afterwards that my going out and playing football with the locals had really led to my being given rather rapid marching orders to move on. In those days Muscat was seen as something of a punishment station, so it all fitted very neatly together.

Herbie Blundell, *a little before, had been shocked by some of the attitudes of the old-style Company.*

I arrived in Bermuda in 1954 on my first posting ... The Manager made us stand up. He was one of the old-fashioned managers: stiff wing collar, bow tie, and from memory a monocle as well, and he said, 'I have to warn you about this island, because you are a passport to the young ladies on this island to get off this island. You have a good job, good company, good prospects. You will meet some very attractive ladies here, but I have to warn you right now, you will meet some that are whiter than you are but their brother is blacker than that telephone.' And that was my introduction. It was quite unbelievable.

I then swapped with a guy, he went to Bermuda and I went to Jamaica, both of us being moved. He was moved because he was engaged to a local Jamaican lady. I was moved because I was enjoying myself too much.

Janet March-Penney*'s story of marrying a Cable & Wireless man has all the elements of romance overcoming tribulation. Coming from the United States, Janet March-Penney found some of the British and the Company ways rather different. After her husband John left the cable ships he joined the foreign staff ashore, and retired in 1968 after a stint as Manager in Peru.*

I went to Puerto Rico in 1941, and I wanted to learn Spanish, so the British Consul's niece invited me into her house. Her mother took me in as a paying guest, so I could speak Spanish all the time ... The Consul invited me along with [his nieces] when they entertained anybody from abroad. One of them came to me one day and said, 'They're entertaining officers off a cable ship, do you want to come?' I had nothing to do, so that was where I met my husband. He was one of the men off the cable ship. We saw quite a bit of each other while the ship was in, then eventually he went off and came back again occasionally. In the meantime, I had to go back to the United States. He came through on his way to England and I saw him again, he met my family, and two years later we got engaged. We were going to be married, but he'd been sent on: not to the States, but to Rio. So I just picked up and went off to Rio to marry him.

It makes me laugh because somewhere along the line somebody in Cable & Wireless made a fuss about somebody going 2,000 miles to be married, and I did much better than that!

But we had a hard time. I arrived on 10 September and the ship didn't come in for ten days, and we'd set the wedding for 30 September. Suddenly somebody in the Embassy woke up to the fact and cabled the Foreign Office – and a reply came back, not possible without an Act of Parliament. It seems there was a Foreign Marriages Act which was to protect youngsters who became enamoured of some local girl, and there had to be a three-week period before you could get married. And we hadn't fulfilled the three-week period. My husband had a pass on Rio Harbour for six months. The ship was all decorated to entertain us ... We did try the Minister of Justice, and he wanted £400 (which we didn't have) to make it official for us to be married, and I didn't want anything that wasn't official because in a foreign country I wasn't taking any chances. Then about two weeks later, the captain offered to take the ship to sea to marry us on board, but then that wasn't on for some reason or other. The troubles we went through to get married, you wouldn't believe. Anyway, finally we *were* married – and then we were called back from our honeymoon, and my husband's ship went away for three months ...

We were somewhere abroad, later, and we met some people who said, 'Oh, you're the poor souls who tried to get married.' I said, 'I do have my wedding lines.' So we were known all over the world pretty well – these were people we'd never met before.

Derek and Elizabeth Moore *met immediately he left England for his first overseas posting, on the Portuguese coast.*

Cable & Wireless had a 200-acre estate on the sea shore at Carcavelos, the centre of this estate was a 200-year old palace, the *Palacio,* in which the Manager lived and had his offices. The cable station was to the seaward side, with various other buildings around, and the Company houses were dotted around the *quinta*, the farm, in amongst pine woods. It was a delightful place, and it was there that I met the girl who got me off the wrong train, at the wrong station, so I married her in a few years.

Elizabeth: My parents worked there, my father owned an engineering company in Portugal, and I went to school there, then to boarding school in England, and after I left school went back there for the holidays. My parents were one of the first outsiders to be members of the Cable & Wireless Club in Carcavelos, so I was always down there, playing tennis, or golf. That is where we met.

Derek: In those days women were not allowed in the bar of the club.

Elizabeth: He used to pass me orange juices out of the window, as I wasn't allowed in. My parents were in there, and they would have been horrified at me being outside.

Derek: But even your mother wasn't allowed in the bar.

John March-Penney's farewell party in Lima on his retirement as Manager in 1958

THE
ROYAL BAN
OF CANADA
JANUARY
26

CHILDREN AND FAMILY

Raising children in overseas locations was often fraught with difficulty, although there could be considerable compensations in the form of the fun that small children especially were able to enjoy. Many parents, because of the peripatetic nature of the father's employment with the Company, chose to have their children educated in boarding schools in Britain. The enforced separations, especially when travel was more difficult and when only one passage a year was paid for by the Company, were difficult for some to bear. The circumstances in which some children were brought into the world were at times equally traumatic.

Maurice Bane *had met his wife in Hong Kong, where she had been a nursing sister. Their first posting as a married couple was to the heat and dust of Aden.*

It wasn't a very enjoyable thought of having a baby in Aden. However the doctor was reassuring, and then we found out that one of the nursing sisters had worked with my wife in Hong Kong. She said, 'Don't worry, I'm in charge of maternity.' The doctor, a graduate of Newcastle, was head of the hospital there in Crater, so we felt reasonably reassured ...

I had to rush out in the middle of the night, get on the telephone – the only telephone was in the office – and tell them we were on the way. When we got there they were waiting to take Mary into the operating theatre to do a Caesarean, and I thought, 'Dear God. Aden. Caesarean section.' Afterwards, the nurse said, 'Well, of course, we had to clear the cats off the operating table' – the hospital was all wide open, you can't believe it unless you've seen it. I was there, the baby was born, and they said, 'You've got a lovely son, and Mary's fine.' ... I went back in the afternoon ... I went to open the gate to go up the steps to where the wards were, and all these damn goats came piling through the gate, they almost knocked me over. They all rushed up and disappeared into various parts of the hospital looking for food. They were allowed to run around. Mary's ward was enclosed, but a lot of it was open, and the goats were wandering eating whatever they could.

Maureen Amor *recalls some of the novelties, the difficulties, and the pleasures for a child of Company parents.*

Our daughter was born in Fayal, and we had the Bishop of Bermuda come to christen her. That was sheer chance ... He stopped off at Fayal, he was passing through. The Azores are in the See of Bermuda. He had to go to a conference and was taking a ship to Lisbon, and it called at the Azores. He came off to see his twenty parishioners, and he did three confirmations. Sue was six months old ... I got a table, and put on a nice white cloth, brass candlesticks and tried to make it much as an altar, and we had the christening out on the verandah. He was absolutely thrilled to bits, said it was the first time he'd ever had a christening on a verandah.

The holy water came out of an old Eastern Telegraph ashtray. They had these big bowl ashtrays you used to fill with sand, beautiful brass like everything else. The ETC logo stamped on it ...

Later on, I felt it would be far too disruptive to our daughter to be hiked here, there and everywhere, not knowing what sort of station you would go to. Like when we were in Zanzibar: there was no school, she'd have had to go to Nairobi anyway. We discussed it with her even before we took her round the schools. We felt that as the Company was getting more and more of the children out for the holidays, we probably wouldn't see her much less [than we had], and it would be more of a settled life for her. Going to school in Britain, she had to change [planes] in Nairobi, so Ted phoned someone in the Company and said, 'Sue's coming through, is it possible for one of the Company to meet her? She has about four hours to kill.' This is what the wives had to do. We did it in Hong Kong, made sure the children were all right. And that was what was so good with the Company, it was very much a family thing. You could go anywhere in the world ... Even if you didn't know them, or perhaps you just knew their name through someone else.

And in Hong Kong – well, heaven help any airline passengers that were on board when it was full of schoolchildren coming out. They used to call it the lollipop flight. British Airways were very good to them, but then they were all Company children, they were all pals and friends, and knew one another.

Elizabeth Moore *was in Fayal, in the Azores, at the same time as Maureen Amor. Her first child was born just before she went there.*

When I went out to Fayal, I had a big Silver Cross pram, and [the baby] was still in it. When I got there, all the children would follow me down the street – it had brakes on it and they thought this was simply marvellous.

But they didn't realise I could understand everything they were saying. 'Where's the engine?' When we left the island, they really didn't mind us leaving – but they wanted us to leave the pram. Which I presume might still be going for all I know.

SOCIAL LIFE

Society was what people made it. In some locations, usually those with the largest or the smallest number of staff, Cable & Wireless staff fitted into existing local society. Elsewhere, especially where language or culture was a real barrier, they were thrown very much upon their own devices. The social life – parties, dinners, junkets on beaches – is the aspect of expatriate life that the world at large sees as a distinguishing feature.

John Davenport *found his social skills being tested.*

Eventually word came through that we were going to the Seychelles, which was terrific. A great place to go. So we packed what little belongings we had and shipped them off to the Seychelles. Then another message came which said, Oops – not the Seychelles, the Cape Verde Islands. And this was typical, this was typical ... There were only twelve British people living there. There were quite a few metropolitan Portuguese, but we didn't mix a lot. So at Christmas you'd attend a round of parties where you'd see the same twelve people. There'd be a Christmas Eve party; there'd be a Christmas lunch party; there'd be a New Year's Eve party. It would be the same twelve people at all these parties. And what we talked about I really can't remember.

Wendy Suart *experienced the Cable & Wireless life in locations both large and small.*

When you've got a primitive station with no amenities you have a very highly developed home social life. Parties in peoples' houses or the Club figured prominently, dances at the Club. Lots of cocktail parties, and parties at people's houses. That's all there was to do.

Colin Stubbs *found like many that the social life in some of the Company's stations could be so vibrant that it was hard to let go.*

Zanzibar, when we left: a little plane flying us into Mombasa, a little crowd seeing us off. We knew the manager of the airline and he said, 'The plane's about to leave, would all passengers come on board?', usual thing. We didn't move. Then another announcement shortly afterwards, 'Flight so and so standing at the tarmac. Would Mr and Mrs Stubbs please board the plane?' Didn't move. Finally he said, 'Would Colin and Pat join the bloody plane?' We didn't want to leave, you see.

Brian Woods *experienced the other side of the coin in Chile in the mid-1960s. On the smallest of the Company's locations life could be almost wholly lacking in sociable companionship.*

I can be quite happy virtually on my own. It could have been an extremely lonely place, Valparaiso, but occasionally there were – very occasionally – various English guys who worked in the Bank of South America. Outside that there were no British people there anyway, and virtually no Americans, who I think foresaw [the Allende revolution]. It was like Bournemouth in the winter. The weather *is* very much like Bournemouth. Later, I went to live in Bournemouth and I thought, 'Gosh, this sea mist that is coming in reminds me of Valparaiso.' No money, and sea mist. And earthquakes.

Richard Selby, *as a young single man abroad in the mid-1960s, tapped into the social rounds that were the backbone of the expatriate life.*

In Bermuda I used to go to church quite regularly and the first occasion I went there, the Manager was sitting in the church. I noticed him up ahead of me, and his wife was there, and they were looking round, and they spotted me. There was some whispering, then his wife got up and came back to me and said, 'David said you can join us if you want.' It was as if I'd been invited to the Royal pew. And I did move up. Let's face it, whether or not you are a deeply religious person, when you're abroad, particularly in those days, as a single person a church is a good way to meet other people – and a good way to get an invite back for Sunday lunch. I got to know quite a few people through the churches in different countries.

Brenda Histed, *in Brazil as a young wife abroad for the first time, swiftly found herself tapped into the other backbone of the expatriate life, the club.*

I thought I was going to live in a grass hut somewhere, I had no idea, we just got on the boat and just went. I didn't even think about it. For the first few months, we lived on tinned peas and meatballs. I can still see the pictures on the tins, you know. Of course, we arrived there with about two and six, we had no money at all, we had to borrow half a month's salary, but we soon got into enjoying the British Country Club. [For] people overseas it's more like family, you become very close friends because you need each other; in fact, I can meet someone I've never met before who's been in Cable & Wireless and you automatically understand each other.

It's the same thing if you meet someone from Shell, BP or ICI who's been overseas: you can instantly communicate because they've had similar experiences. One of the things you hear sometimes is a lot of criticism about the grandiose life that expatriates live. But if you think about it, the club, or club life, becomes your extended family. If you live in this country you've got aunts and uncles, that's your extended family; and if you want baby-sitters and what have you, you get it from your friends and relations of long standing. Whereas when you're overseas, the way you establish a group is by going to, if you like, the local British club. I've heard lots of people who quite openly criticise this club life, but it does become a very important part. It's not a snobbish thing, because the Americans have their club, any nationality

Senior local Cable & Wireless personnel among the guests at an embassy party in Indonesia, 1952

has its club. Lebanese clubs used to be very big, and very good. It's where people of different nationalities get together, where they can have something in common.

Janet March-Penney*'s memories are rather less sunny. She and many other Company wives often felt themselves to be living on the fringes of a male-dominated system.*

The Company was utterly and completely unconcerned about the wives, and yet those men got places because we women stood behind them, and entertained for them. We practically deserved an income of our own – but people in those days didn't take consideration of that.

Wendy Suart *experienced the pleasures and the tribulations of being a family alone where her husband, Brian, was the Engineer at the Mount Butler short-wave radio receiving station in Hong Kong.*

We were on the top of this windblown mountain at Mount Butler and we were lords of all we surveyed. There were no other Europeans within a couple of miles, we had a dozen Chinese workmen who lived on the mountain; others would come up by Company van in the morning ... There were no children for my kids to play with, we were very solitary. But it was a wonderful, lovely place with wild flowers growing and streams running down the valleys and even pools where the kids could swim. Well, dip. I enjoyed Mount Butler very much. But nothing would grow up there ... At Mount Butler we were frustrated because as soon as plants reached the top of a low retaining wall the wind would go *phut phut* and cut them off. It was virtually impossible to grow a garden there.

In February, March, the end of winter, beginning of summer, the warm air comes into Hong Kong and hits the cold continental air – and you get fog.

From a thousand feet up you get fog, so The Peak is always completely covered in mist, and on Mount Butler which was a thousand feet we were also in the fog. Sometimes it wouldn't lift for a week. If you look out of your windows and see nothing but white cotton wool, after a day or two you begin to feel very odd indeed. You think, 'I can't see anything, therefore there is nothing out there. There is simply nothing out there. I am simply living alone here ...' One day I had had enough of this and I thought I must get out, I must get out and go somewhere, so I wrapped the kids up in coats and scarves and hoods and gloves, hopped in the car and we drove down the mountain. We just drove out of the Company property. Only a hundred, two hundred feet lower down it was like a knife, the edge of the fog, and there was Hong Kong sitting bathed in sunlight ... After an hour [of visiting other, somewhat surprised people] I thought we'd better get back. I drove back, and I thought it would be clear now. I drove through the gates and down came the curtain, thick, thick, thick. I said to Brian at lunchtime, 'You wouldn't believe it but there was beautiful sunshine down there and they were swimming.' Absolutely appalling.

Later on, as the Manager's wife in Jamaica, I was determined that no wife should be solitary and I instituted coffee parties ... I let it be known that the first Wednesday in the month or whatever, there would be coffee at my house – but you didn't have to come. So they used to trot in and we used to have a ball: we'd have shower parties, baby parties for pregnant mums, and all that sort of thing.

Elizabeth and Derek Moore *were at the sharp end of party-giving and party-receiving when Derek was Manager of various Cable & Wireless places, in the Caribbean and the Arabian Gulf, in the 1960s, and Elizabeth had to cope with the social round.*

The social life on Montserrat was difficult in that they were all retired, mainly Americans and Canadians, who would get up at eleven, drink, have their lunch, sleep all afternoon, and then from 5 o'clock they were ready to have a party again. If you were both working ... it was a little bit difficult. Three cocktail parties a week, sometimes more. There were British companies as well, and we had dinner parties, but the Americans just loved cocktail parties. The first party we went to, on a boat, we thought this was absolutely fantastic – at the start we got given two drinks and two lifebelts – but we did get fed up with it.

Derek: After three years' teaching in Porthcurno and being desperately hard up – we hadn't bought a bottle of gin in three years – we were lying there under the tropical sky floating in the water with our gins next to us ... Now, Doha was a place where the social life was heavy – there you could have four or five cocktail parties *a day*. In fact, on one occasion we got so fed up with the cocktail parties we loaded up the car, put a mattress in the back, drove out to the sand dunes, got off the road and hid in the sand dunes. We had a barbecue ... and slept the night there. It was a fantastic thing – waking up with the sun just coming up over the sand dunes, it was something you just couldn't describe. That was to avoid cocktail parties.

COLONIAL WAYS

The whole structure of the Cable & Wireless telecommunications system was based within Britain's imperial sphere. Almost everywhere that the map was coloured pink, Cable & Wireless were also to be found, both for commercial traffic and for official communications; the picture was similar in South America, where Britain had established 'informal empire' in the nineteenth century. The Dominions – Australia, Canada, South Africa – had been the first to break away from this system. In the 1960s the winds of change blew through the Cable & Wireless system as they blew through other aspects of Britain's life and colonial rule overseas.

John Packer *explains the quasi-colonial aspects of the Cable & Wireless system, and describes one of the very last surviving examples of that life during his time spent in the mid-1970s in the British Solomon Islands in the western Pacific.*

The overseas life of Cable & Wireless was akin to the Colonial Service. The engineers who travelled around the world were doing it in the company of District Officers, District Commissioners and people of this kind. In some cases these were people on a similar social level, these were the people you socialised with (beyond the level of the very junior technicians), and it was, if you like, a part of the Colonial Service. A British way of life – not a specifically Cable & Wireless sort of thing. Stiff upper lip, show the locals that we're British, we can cope, and all of this.

It was the dying days of empire, that coincided with the dying days of the old cable technology. The two things went hand in hand. What was coming in was the days of independence, and with it new technologies. And a new lifestyle. Instead of Company staff doing a two-year overseas tour, it was more doing a short stint helping the local staff who were now the technicians, operators, engineers. They were coming to Porthcurno and then going back and carrying on. Gradually more and more of the staff on the overseas stations, the posts – junior levels, gradually working up to more senior levels and today management levels – were the local people. All very right and proper ...

Of all the places I'd been to – East Africa, West Africa, Ascension Island, the Middle East – the Solomon Islands were the most different in terms of going back in time. East Africa or West Africa, you go out into the villages and you see bits of corrugated iron; Solomon Islands' houses were built of the local material, the roofs with banana leaves or thatch of various kinds, the sides were built with the trunks of sago palms and this sort of thing ... As recently as the mid-1970s, we were still in the old colonial, empire mode, even though the Prime Minister was a Solomon Islander. There was the expatriate society and there was the local society. And partly due to language difficulties there wasn't a great deal of socialising between the two. [My wife and I] moved in both circles. But to a large number of expatriates there was the G Club, where you went for your gin and tonic or your swim in the pool, and you whiled away your leisure hours there. You went to work in the bank or whatever it was that took you to the islands in the first place, and longed for the day that you could get out of this very, very hot and unhealthy atmosphere when your furlough, your leave, was due ...

There were expatriates from many different countries; it wasn't a British expatriate community in quite the same way that some of the other places had been, like Ascension or Aden. There were quite a number of Australians and New Zealanders there ... [Japanese mining and] tuna-fishing industry. There were various banks, Hong Kong & Shanghai Bank and so on. There were all sorts of staff whose companies or base of operations were South-East Asian rather than European, simply because the Solomon Islands are down there.

I've always been, as has my wife, interested in travel, geography, natural history. And so we did go to the G Club, and had a good time there, having a swim and so on. We also spent a lot of our time exploring, and visiting the outer islands. The opportunity arose partly because we moved in both circles. We had met both Solomon Islanders and people doing translation work, translating the local languages – of which there were many – into English, for Bible translation and so on. We were able to visit some of these good folk on very remote islands where they were perhaps the only European family on the whole island. This is why we got the very strong sense that nothing had changed there since the time of Captain Cook, once you had got out of Honiara. In Honiara you'd got buses and bicycles and this rather ramshackle town with remnants of World War Two, but on the outer islands it was quite, quite different.

Things were so limited in the local shops. I remember hearing word that the Mendana Stores had cheese. Not any particular cheese, Blue Stilton or whatever, but just cheese. And rushing home to Lorna saying, 'Hey, they've got cheese down at the Mendana,' and she got in the car and shot down and we had cheese. The first time we'd had cheese for many weeks. The island ran out of toilet rolls once – all these things came in by sea – and you just had to make do and mend. The culture shock was when we came home: we visited relatives in Worthing, Sussex, a fairly big and well-equipped town, where Lorna went into a supermarket to buy some toothpaste. She had to come out again. There was too much, she was bewildered. She said, 'Not only have you got toothpaste, but which to choose out of 72 different styles? Did you want it with fluoride, which flavour, did you want it multicoloured ...?' This was such a shock: we realised that despite the moans and complaints how remarkably well off we are in this country. Life overseas makes one appreciate in a way that perhaps people – people who haven't lived away for a long time but have simply been on holiday – forget what a variety of things we have.

Wendy Suart *remembers vividly the social niceties of life under British colonial protection in North Borneo (now Sabah) in the early 1950s.*

There was still the colonial business about signing the Governor's book on arrival, and you had to sign it after you had had hospitality from the Governor. If you went to a cocktail party, or were sufficiently senior to rate a dinner party, you never asked the Governor back. He was never allowed to dine out at ordinary people's houses. So a way of repaying his hospitality was to sign his book the morning after. Sometimes I would forget, and it would be two days later and I would falsify the date. I would go back later to look at it and the Private Secretary had corrected the date. So I had been found out.

After dinner there, ladies would go upstairs with the Governor's wife to her bedroom. The men would go out and face into a hedge, their white dinner jackets gleaming in the dark. This was known variously as 'inspecting the cannas', 'going out on the coral' or 'planter's privilege'. During my time there the Archbishop of Canterbury made a visit. And the young Duke of Kent, who was then 16, and his mother Princess Marina came out to visit. I often wondered if they were taken out to the hedge after dinner. So it was a cross between extreme formality, and great informality in other ways.

Chris Schofield, *like many Cable & Wireless personnel stationed on remote islands, received very occasional visits from Her Majesty's official representatives.*

The District Commissioner was over on Fanning Island one Christmas. He was a youngster, no problem. But after his visit we had the Resident Commissioner come up. He had been to Fanning previously, complete with sword, cocked hat and the trimmings; and rather than land at the commercial jetty and be driven up, he decided to come ashore at the cable station with all pomp and ceremony. Apparently, they had all the Gilbertese lined up, and the postmaster, and the policeman. A guard of honour. The whaler came up, hit the beach, and he was standing at the front and stepped out. Unfortunately, he missed his footing at this point, a wave turned up and he was down in the waves, plumed hat, sword, the lot. The Gilbertese just howled their heads off, they thought this was the funniest thing that had happened since the previous comedy film, so the next time he came, he came down to the commercial landing, and turned up in just normal whites, no pomp and ceremony.

Maurice Bane, *ten years or so before that incident, had seen evidence of how it was not just Cable & Wireless personnel who became somewhat strange when left on an island almost on their own – and then how much the colonial lifestyle was fully operational east of Suez in the late 1940s and early 1950s.*

Before reaching Aden there was Kameran Island. It's a small island in the middle of the Red Sea and there's nothing much there, I don't remember hills or mountains at all. The District Officer or Commissioner came out, terribly resplendent in his white uniform, collar up round his neck, my first touch of the British Raj overseas. As you came to the airport entrance there was a large notice which said 'one way traffic only: 30 miles an hour', and we went in from the airport to this small village, and all along this sandy road there were traffic signs. And yet there were no cars except the Administrator's car, which was a battered old thing, and apparently, he was a complete nut. He'd had all these traffic signs dotted all over the island. He'd obviously been there too long. I couldn't believe it: this dusty, sandy road, no tarmacadam or anything, and all these traffic signs. 30 miles an hour, and not another car in sight.

Then I got to Aden and there was nobody to meet me at the airport, obviously they hadn't been told I was coming. There were these broken-down taxis at the airstrip with just a small hut. I went to one of these broken-down taxis, and I said, 'Cable & Wireless.' He said, 'Huh?' I said, 'You take me to Cable & Wireless?' All this chattering went on, 'No sir, no understand.' 'Well, look, Cable & Wireless, Eastern.' 'Ah! *Telegraph Englesee.*' 'Yes,' so we had clicked. I climbed into his taxi, he drove me out of the airport, and I arrived at this rather splendid tropical mess with one or two green things hanging round the entrance, and there I was at Eastern Telegraph.

I went in through the porch, there didn't seem to be anybody about (it was about 2 o'clock in the afternoon), when suddenly a chap came weaving through the door, in broken-down sandals and scruffy shorts, and a scruffy old shirt which seemed to have rips in it. He said, 'Who are you?' I said, 'I'm Maurice Bane. I've just been sent here, I've just been appointed here.' 'Oh, you're the new boy are you? My name's Bertie Bardens. Come in and have a drink?' I thought, 'I don't know, they've gone native here.' We went on to a large verandah, lovely style, he said, 'We drink pink gins here,' so I said, 'OK, a pink gin.' And they rustled me up a little curry for lunch. He said, 'Now you're here, are you interested in poetry?' I said, 'Well, yes, I am as a matter of fact.' 'Good. Your room's up here somewhere.' So we tramped across this square, and up some steps, and up more steps,

The heat and dust of Aden in the 1940s

and up to this long building with lots of rooms, and right up to the end. That was old Bertie Bardens's place, and we sat there for the rest of the afternoon drinking pink gin while he read to me his poetry. I thought, 'At last I've arrived, this is the East' ...

It got to sundown and suddenly I heard voices going 'Boy', and I thought 'What was that?' Everybody had a room boy, and these boys appeared with a tray, of Scotch, or gin. So you didn't drink – after you'd had your lunchtime gin – until the sun went down over Little Aden, which was about 6 o'clock in the evening, and then the voices would roar out.

We lived in these large buildings which had been built, I should think, in the 1880s when the first cables went through ... There had been an enormous staff of operators, and they had to house all these people, so there were two enormous blocks. How else can I explain Aden? There was this dusty cratered bowl, barren, except just one period during the year when the rains would come. Suddenly all the rock and lava would spring with small flowers, and there was a carpet of green with flowers. It was beautiful, but then of course, it would die very quickly. Then you got the Hamseen, the wind that came off the desert, and the dust flew in, and it filled everything: your teeth, your rooms ...

[Travelling further east] I went to the Gall Face Hotel in Colombo: beautiful old colonial buildings, high ceilings, and beyond, a swimming pool. And this was my first sight of somebody in a swimming pool being served a drink. We changed and came out and I looked, and there was this waiter at the end, in a turban, with a large silver tray, and there were two blokes standing at the end of the pool, up to their waist in water, taking their drinks off the tray. I thought, *this* is the Far East. This is what I've read about. Somerset Maugham, all that ...

On P&O ships going to the Far East, you'd see a nondescript crowd of people boarding the ship, your baggage going somewhere else, the officers at the gangway – 'Good *afternoon*, sir,' and people more or less crawling onto the boat. You thought they were just a crowd of people. And yet they were old colonials: the second day out, when the sun came out, they were like a bunch of chameleons. They'd all appear in their splendid blazers, with inscriptions on their pockets, and cravats in their necks, and they all seemed to be terribly,

terribly county. All forming their groups – in no time at all you'd find the senior ones would get the groups together, and the ladies would form their own circle if the wives were on board ... I remember reading an article later on by someone who saw the experience in the same light as I did: the chameleon effect of the British Colonial.

'FATHER EASTERN'

The Eastern Telegraph Company, one of the constituent parts of Cable & Wireless and the backbone of both the Company and its profitability, was fiercely jealous of its traditions. Mess living, silver, the formality of overseas life. The paternalism inherent in its ethos is represented by its affectionate nickname, Father Eastern. The other side of paternalism was adherence to a code both written and unwritten of hierarchy and seniority. It was to modern eyes an intensely old-fashioned institution: promotion came through the ranks, men waited to fill dead men's shoes, pay was low but privileges were substantial.

John Howie *recalls mess life in Port Sudan.*

It was just being part of the family. We – I – felt that whatever happened old Father Eastern would look after me. I don't suppose he would have hauled me out of gaol if I'd got stuck in there, but at least if I fell ill or anything went wrong, I would get sympathetic treatment. It was a sort of family atmosphere. It was very much so in Port Sudan. We used to turn out if there was a problem in the office ...

In Port Sudan if you wanted dinner you had to be dressed. All day you ambled around in shorts and a shirt, but if you wanted to have dinner you dressed. And luckily dress in Port Sudan was a white shirt with a bow tie, black cummerbund, white trousers, black shoes and socks. That was Red Sea rig. When we had dances it was quite colourful because all the different departments had their own colour cummerbunds. In-house ours were black; but when we went out to a party we put on scarlet ones. That being the ETC colour. And then the Veterinary Service had yellow, and the Medical Service had maroon, and the Sudan Railways had green, and the Police had blue. So all the men used to look quite snappy. But I suppose those traditions have disappeared too.

And you had to have a tied bow tie. Woe betide anyone who had a made-up one. It used to be pulled off his neck. You had to have a proper one.

Ted Amor *and many like him in the 1940s hoped that they would be successful when they had finished their initial training course in being posted overseas to the traditional stations of the Eastern Telegraph Company.*

The lore of the company was all there, and my pal and I, we both wanted Eastern. We'd been dragged up on Kipling, and we all imagined ourselves walking down the Maidan in Calcutta. Fortunately we were both Eastern. My posting at Suez was one of the old Eastern stations – they used to call it the Cook's Tour, which was Malta, Alex[andria], Suez, Port Sudan, Aden. People used to circulate up and down those places. So I landed at Suez, and although of course all the big operating staffs had gone years ago, in the thirties, it was an old Eastern station, down to the very last detail ...

Then I was met at Alexandria and taken to spend the night in Alexandria mess. Mess? Oh dear no ... The luxury of the place. The furniture, the gleaming white tablecloths, the servants, and wall after wall covered in silver, mess silver. An entirely new world after spending all my student days in the students' hostel, and the lodgings at Porthcurno which weren't much better. Gosh! And the whole world seemed to open up.

Lounging on the verandah in Labuan.
A photograph from the old colonial days of the 1920s

Wendy Suart, *in the larger staff in Hong Kong, in the early 1950s, was acutely aware of the niceties associated with the notion of seniority and the sequence of professional grades that were used for the foreign service staff.*

As a junior engineer, Brian was sent as an engineer in charge of the Mount Butler Receiving Station on top of a lonely windswept hill. Again, I was the only woman there. I then became embroiled in a large Company staff, at that stage there were about sixteen Cable & Wireless people. Seven years later, when Brian returned as General Manager, he had up to a hundred on the staff and the whole thing had burst, the balloon was going up and Hong Kong was booming.

I began to be aware that the Manager would hold dinners for 'P.G. Cornish and up' and 'P. G. Cornish and down'. P. G. Cornish was a man who was 3rd grade in the Company hierarchy, and he was the dividing line. He went to both parties. P. G. Cornishes and up, and P. G. Cornishes and down; we were, of course, down. My husband being 4th grade. He had just passed his general exam which was the final hurdle and opened the way to future promotion.

I'd heard wonderful stories about other managers and their wives in other postings, where the manager's wife would be so obsessed with grade. One came to a friend of mine there who was on the staff: 'Mr Jones who is 2nd grade is leaving, so we're having a gathering for him and I've asked Mr Smith, 3rd, and I thought we'd perhaps have Mr Brown along, 2nd grade,' and this sort of thing. To refer to it in conversation I thought was so laughable. I very early on lost my awe of Company grades. But many people did go in great awe of the Company grading system.

Derek and Elizabeth Moore *saw these niceties in operation even amid the almost-lunar landscape of Ascension Island.*

The Assistant Manager on Ascension Island was Justice of the Peace, the Manager was a Magistrate. In his office he had two desks, one for

Manager of Cable & Wireless and one for the Magistrate, and he would walk from one to the other depending on what was happening.

Elizabeth: The Manager was very strict, he kept to the rules. If you went to a dinner party there, it depended on your position in the Company whether you left first, and when you left. It even got to the stage of when you went to the toilet after dinner: the most important, senior person went first, and then down in rank. He was very keen on that. You must always have a little silver tray outside your front door so he could leave his card.

Derek: Unless he could leave his card and you left your card you didn't get invited anywhere. Victorian almost.

Jim Bairstow *was a member of the contingent from Australia and New Zealand recruited in 1944 to form part of the TELCOM brigade that brought communications to liberated South-East Asia. They found these notions of seniority and formality puzzling to the point of disbelief.*

For many of [the Australasians] the atmosphere, the *colonial* atmosphere was certainly a negative point. It's true there was a difference in attitude between the few Australian staff abroad with Cable & Wireless at that time ... and, seen from an Australian point of view, the stuffier attitude of the staff who came from the UK. It becomes a matter of diplomacy how to put it. Many of the Australasians, perhaps particularly the young ones, were not prepared to accept the strong seniority connotations which existed in the Company at that time. I can remember many upsets in messes because of a fundamental difference in the attitude of the two groups.

In the army camp in Ceylon with the New Zealanders and the Australians, the New Zealanders were put in one hut as a dormitory and the Australians were put in another one. So there was always a certain amount of rivalry between the Australians and New Zealanders ... Then the young English

AND WIRELESS LIMITED.
CABLE AND WI
ADIOTELEPHONE

The Cable & Wireless offices in Hong Kong: the exterior of Jardine House c. 1960

chaps came out and introduced the concept of seniority. One young chap was faced with a new arrival saying, 'I'm senior to you, I want that bed space, you have to move,' and was shattered to be met with the response, colloquially, 'Up yours, Jack.' He didn't understand what he'd come up against. We didn't quite speak the same language.

Maurice Bane*'s fears about breaking, even unwittingly, the unwritten rules of seniority in Hong Kong were to prove unfounded, but he was alarmed all the same.*

My wife has a good taste of colour, and it was time every six years to refurbish [the accommodation]. Mary went out and bought curtains, had the chairs recovered, put loose covers on them. She went to this shop she knew, and she chose a rather lovely blue and white fabric. There was a senior Company wife, in fact the Divisional Manager's wife, there looking ... 'What are you selecting?' So Mary said, 'I rather like that.' 'Oh, you can't have that because that's the one I've chosen.' So Mary said, 'But I've already placed the order.' 'Oh. Well, perhaps we'll have to order something else.' When Mary came home and told me I said, 'That's it, darling, the Divisional Manager will have us out within a week. You've taken away the curtains and cushion covers from the DM's wife. Very amusing.'

In contrast to the life in stations around the world, work and life in London seemed radically different. Many foreign service staff spent periods of time working in London – and many disliked it – while there was widespread resentment in the field of the degree of centralised control the Company's Head Office exercised. That is the nature of the relationship between the periphery and the core in many highly centralised operations, but nonetheless the difficulties were experienced and voiced intensely.

George Warwick, *who ended his years in the Company running its largest and most profitable foreign base, Hong Kong, has had many occasions to reflect on the quintessential nature of the business that the old Cable & Wireless ran.*

In the bad old days you didn't have a Manager, you had a Supervisor and he took his instructions from London ... They changed it to Manager, because it was more in line with modern thinking, but of course you really needed to change the job as well as the title. Hardly anyone working in London, and supposed to be running it, had ever been to a station. You very rarely got anyone from overseas staff working back in London, and very rarely did they make visits – before the advent of frequent air travel, it was very difficult.

It was a funny way to run a business. But, you see, when it went back to the old cable system, it was a *perfect* way to run a business.

You laid the cables and you had a network of cables. The operation of those cables was controlled by an office in London. Whenever you got a cable failure it was reported back. This was a 24-hours-a-day thing. Instructions were sent: which cables would be diverted and which way the traffic would flow. Within an hour or so of the cable breaking, in nearly every case things were back to normal as far as the customer was concerned. These instructions would come out – even the gear ratios you put in the machines to get the speed right. It worked a treat. But then, we controlled all those stations. As soon as somewhere became independent, or you were working through someone you didn't control, you couldn't send out and say, Do this. It was, Please do this, or, Will you do this?

Ken Reece *was recruited locally as an engineer in his native Barbados. Like many who had had no connection with London and the ways the old Company operated, he found and still finds the degree of centralisation perplexing, and wryly amusing at the same time.*

Cable & Wireless in those days, let's say the colonial days ... Everything down to toilet paper came from London. There was a toilet paper, brand name Bronco, wax paper. It would probably suit now for wrapping things up in. Who could have invented that as a toilet paper? All these things were sent. That's ridiculous. And ladies' uniforms. They had no choice. The colour, battleship grey. Those were grey dim days in the office, it's not even like they had pastel shades: the equipment was battleship grey, and somebody said the equipment should match the walls so the walls were either painted grey or dark, dismal blue. Pens. The ink. Everything was brought from London. Nobody considered if it was suitable for the tropics or not. 'This is what we have in the UK, and this is what you should use there.' But times change.

Patricia Bosdet, *who joined the financial and accounting departments of Cable & Wireless, recalls all the gradations of seniority that were just as much part of the Head Office picture as they were in the grand old stations of the Eastern Telegraph Company. These memories come from the 1960s.*

There was a very strong structure in terms of hierarchy. You started off from a junior position, and as you went up, if you got to a certain position, you got a chair with arms on, which meant you'd achieved something. The level above that, you had a square of carpet that you would put your chair with arms on. You had what in those days were called officials: senior management who had little offices. If they wanted to talk to somebody, they had a series of little bells that they pressed, like you used to summon maids. Press the buzzer and the bell rings. If they wanted to talk to somebody in the ships section they would press the little buzzer and the senior man in the section would trot along to talk to them. If he wasn't there, then the second in command would go in, and then the third in command. And if everybody else had gone to lunch then it would be me ...

At about 4.45 each day all of the Directors would come from their floor, and there was a big car outside, and they all used to pile into this car. The

Telegram girls in Electra House

chauffeur used to take them all round the London stations and drop them off one by one; and I think in the mornings he would go round and collect them. There was never any suggestion they would stay for an extra half an hour and do something, or that they might have their own chauffeur or their own car. They would always pile in this car. It would have been quite cramped.

But you didn't think it particularly odd, it was what happened. I think it was very structured and bureaucratic, but you didn't mind that: in many ways it created the structure. You knew who was boss. There was still a certain friendship there, because the people who were at the top had worked their way up through the Company, they didn't come in from outside.

There was a trade-off between this sense of hierarchy and belonging, and the financial recompense that went with it. The contrasts were all the more pronounced in South America, where the Western Telegraph Company was the principal operator, but there was widespread feeling that levels of pay were insufficient.

Wally Hardiman *spent the greater part of his working life with the Company selling and promoting its services in South America.*

The older staff in Brazil, pre-War, during the War and just after the War, were far worse off than they were in the Eastern Telegraph Company. The Western Telegraph Company's conditions weren't as good as the Eastern companies. A quirk of fate ...

After 1925 or 1926, the Company hardly ever owned accommodation in Brazil. It was always rented. Whereas in the Eastern they had all the Company houses, all the messes: Gibraltar, Aden, Singapore, Seychelles ... we were told to go and find our own apartment when we got married. You were given a ceiling, you couldn't go above the ceiling, and that was it ... We started on £100 a year in 1944 and when we went abroad – I went abroad in May 1945 on £115 plus £24 foreign service allowance – that was £140 a year. Then we were accommodated in a mess, and our mess bill was probably about 30 bob (£1.50) a week ... They hadn't put up any salary scales from about 1930, but they were giving bonuses and our last bonus was about 80 per cent of the year's salary. Our last bonus was in 1947/8. That was when we were nationalised ... From then onwards our salaries started to meet commercial standards. I would say more commercial standards: in Brazil for many years we were always considered worse off than the banks. Lloyds Bank, British American Tobacco, Shell, people like that: they were well paid. We were always below, but we were better paid than the smaller companies, the merchant companies – importers and exporters – except for the coffee people, they were extremely well paid.

I think all over the world our salaries were probably slightly less than the top echelon of companies. But we had security of tenure which was a great thing.

John Bragg *led a life in various postings that may best be described as unconventional. Many of the ways he found to make ends meet were also unconventional.*

Barbados is of course a fabulous island; but what they paid you in Cable & Wireless there was almost a pittance, so I needed to find some other means of supplementing my pay. For the nearly three years which I spent there I got into running some slot machines and a couple of ice cream trucks which made up my income.

I was working day shifts. I was working some nights, but the weekends I always gave away to other people ... which left me more time to look after the slot machine routes – these were in rum shops, bars, in Barbados. It started with somebody looking for a technician, a technical guy to look after these slot machines. So it went from there: from being involved, to actually running the things. Towards the end, when I was leaving Barbados I had to get rid of all that. A Canadian guy who came in took it over.

I don't think the Company were overjoyed. The Manager there wrote a letter back to Head Office, because when I got back I was told by the Staff Manager at that time, unless I picked up or improved my ways they would probably have to ask for my resignation. So in disgrace I was sent out to Manila as a watchkeeper. That was seen as a punishment.

Pete Wolfe *found that although the Manager of the particular station he had been on during the mid-1950s had been able to run the place in an autocratic way, making the question of pay and conditions even more vexed, the mechanisms existed within the Company to redress injustices.*

I came home on leave in 1957 and I went up to the Staff Manager. He said, 'Hello, Wolfe. Had a good tour?' I said, 'Have I bloody hell!' 'Right. Sit down and tell me all about it.' And I was with him for two hours telling him what was going on ... A few weeks later I got a letter from one of the engineers like myself. He said, 'I don't know what you said in Head Office, Pete, but there's been hell to pay here.' He said, 'The manager has been demoted. Three blokes who have been here twenty years, ex-London staff, have been transferred. All our duties have been changed to comply with the overseas rulebook. Our allowances have all been increased, the new manager has to send in a monthly budget of costs so that we can be adjusted. We get overtime full rate.' And he said, 'Thanks very much, we're all laughing our heads off.'

Wendy Suart *recalls how the mismatch between status and earnings overseas really came to matter, when the foreign service staff reached their retirement and returned to Britain.*

We were very fortunate in having 'millionaire living', but we had very little in our pockets. We had the servants, the house, the driver, all the perks that go with a managerial position – but we had no money. At that stage the F1 salaries were still quite low. When we left [Hong Kong] in 1974 we came home, and we couldn't raise the deposit for a house here, a simple little, unpretentious estate house. It was ludicrous because the vendor, who

Maureen Amor's servants in St Vincent, Cape Verde Islands

was desperately trying to sell, said, 'Would you like me to lend you the deposit?' The vendor!

But had we done one more tour we'd have been rolling, because that year the F1 staff's pay just went *whoom* and rocketed. We heard about people in the Gulf sending home their monthly salary to bank and living on allowances. Everyone had so much more money after that. We were hearing about our contemporaries in Hong Kong and they were all so rich, and we felt a bit sad about that. But what the hell, you can't take it with you.

TEAM PLAYERS

In the old-style Cable & Wireless, the principal theme that the staff internalised from the very beginning of their training was that the service was paramount. Getting the message through was the reason for their existence, and they had to pull together to achieve that. It was an ethos that seems to have run throughout the Company. Eccentricity and individualism were widely tolerated, but not at the expense of the service.

Ron Werngren, *in asking himself what was the main characteristic of the employees of Cable & Wireless, has practical and philosophical approaches to the question.*

The Brazilian network was very extensive, went up the coast. They in the nicest possible way were a law unto themselves. They had so much traffic that at certain times of the day we were straight through to New York, but at other times we were broken in Rio, and they would take us off on a perforated tape. New York was very important for commodities: coffee from Rio and meat from Buenos Aires. Your best customers expected a reply in five minutes. A reply. They would phone or teletype it in and expect a reply back on the teleprinter in five minutes; if it wasn't, if they made a complaint that it was more than five

The 'spaghetti' of cables on Muscat

minutes, you were writing memos all over the place. Of course, time was of the essence: they were trying to get in on particular prices and so on. I maintain that we gave, in the telegraph system, a Rolls Royce service, because it was expensive, but once you'd paid your money, then you could ask any question, get any answer you liked. The after-sales service if you like was very good.

The Cable & Wireless 'type' is somebody who will try to be reliable, is happy to be of service. Because that's all we are. We're a service. And somebody who doesn't mind learning as he goes along. Doesn't that sound horrible? It's somebody who certainly has to adapt, but not too much, and somebody who has certain standards. Not necessarily terribly high, but standards they will be: so far, no further. If we're in a group together there are certain things that are unsaid. We're talking about this happened and that happened and we never stop to think, why did that happen that way? We *know* why it happened that way. We aren't all paragons of virtue, or terribly intelligent. Maybe we were brainwashed at Porthcurno into the idea of service, it could be as simple as that. More or less isolated. And the whole idea was 'the exigencies of the service'. The service came first, always.

There must be a sameness among us somewhere. You'll probably find the sameness is in what is not said as much as what is said.

Herbie Blundell *sums up.*

It sounds daft to say in this day and age, but there were a fair number of free spirits there, no doubt about that. All the guys I knew ... I think they'd go anywhere and do anything. It sounds contradictory: a lot of them were highly individualistic, but also good team players. If they had one ability it was that they could talk to anybody. Didn't matter if it was the Chairman, the Governor-General, or the hall porter, they could get on with them and talk to them and understand them. That key characteristic of being able to adapt.

CHAPTER THREE

Island life: Ascension and Cocos

Ascension really was *a place. You could say it was the back end of beyond but the majority who went there thoroughly enjoyed it. Most of it was lava, very little greenery. You either took it with you and you made it, or you couldn't abide it. The people there made it enjoyable.*

George Warwick

It was rare indeed for a member of the foreign service staff of Cable & Wireless not to spend at least part of his working life on a small island. Somewhere in the Caribbean, or far out in one of the oceans. Grand Turk, Rodrigues, Fanning, St Thomas, Diego Garcia, St Vincent, Ascension, Cocos. Special reserves of fortitude were needed for some of these islands, where conditions were spartan and contact with the outside world sporadic – except for the constant telecommunications traffic whether by submarine cable, wireless or satellite.

Ascension Island is one of the defining places for Cable & Wireless. At one time, as we have seen, the Manager was also the Resident Magistrate. Its remote position in the middle of the South Atlantic was counterbalanced by its crucial position as a telecommunications crossroads, first with cables and subsequently satellite communications. Its strategic importance was recognised in wartime (see pp 136–8); the United States used it as a military outpost and as a station for tracking the space ventures of the 1960s and 1970s. Ascension was a place that people either came to love, or swiftly came to hate.

The cable between the Cape and Australia was laid by the Eastern Extension company in 1901, via Mauritius, the nearby island of Rodrigues, across the Indian Ocean to the Cocos (Keeling) Islands, and down to Fremantle, Western Australia. Forty acres on Direction Island, one of twenty-seven tiny islands in the group, were leased from the Clunies-Ross family, self-styled 'Kings of Cocos'. The islands became an Australian territory at the end of 1955. The Clunies-Ross ownership ended in 1978. Cocos, the Keeling-Cocos Islands, Cocos & Keeling Islands, the Cocos (Keeling) Islands. Whatever the name, it was one of the most isolated of all postings for men from Cable & Wireless. Within the Company, it was sometimes viewed as a 'punishment' station, a place where those who had transgressed might be sent. For those who went there, the reality was sometimes more pleasant than the myth.

Cocos's position gave it a strategic importance in telecommunications, especially in both World Wars when it was also a vital transport link. Cable & Wireless left Cocos in 1956, when Australia took over, and the cable chain on which the Company's presence was based was finally abandoned.

The late **Brian Suart** *passed through Ascension during the Second World War, as a staging post for the Far East.*

Ascension Island. Eight degrees south of the equator – right in the middle. The nearest land is 750 miles away and that's St Helena, where Napoleon was exiled. It's about five miles by six, and looks like a bit of the moon, most of it, but it has a nice green mountain in the middle that goes up to 3,000 feet. It's a very interesting place, a wonderful place for a fisherman – which I'm not. There's a lot of bird life as well as all sorts of fish. It's a thousand miles from land of any size ... I went to Ascension in the bomb bays of a Liberator which was going back the other way. Took another fellow and myself, and the mail bag. I think they were as worried as we were as whether or not we would find it. It is very small.

Derek and Elizabeth Moore *count Ascension as one of the very happiest postings they had with Cable & Wireless when they were there in the later 1950s. Ascension was a place where wives and families could live, unlike Cocos except in the very last years of its use by the Company.*

Oh, Ascension *looks* godforsaken, yes. It had a lovely climate: you imagine, around 80, 82 degrees with almost no humidity.

Ascension Island painted by Peter Critchley, the island farmer from the late 1950s to the early 1970s

Elizabeth: The few roads were tarmaced, white stones each side always kept beautifully white. Our gardens were clinker, and we had big round oil drums for trees. A magnificent flamboyant and other trees outside that we used to water with the bathwater. Kept to water our plants. It was always very neat and tidy. And we had our little shop, the canteen, where we used to be able to go and buy our bits and pieces. All our vegetables came down from Green Mountain, that Peter Critchley used to organise. It depended on the size of your family how much you were allowed to have. Meat and so on, again it depended on the size of your family ...

Derek: If you ignore the cockroaches and that, it was a lovely island. We had no money: we never carried money with us. We went to the Exiles Club for a drink, signed a chit, at the end of the month you got a piece of paper saying you'd got so much left over.

Elizabeth: I always remember, once my houseboy went home on leave. I hadn't got anybody, he said, 'I'll arrange for Francis to come to you.' So I said to Derek, 'I'm going to have Francis for a week or two.' Then I suddenly realised that Francis was the frou-frou [night soil] man. Derek said, 'No matter, he'll scrub his hands when he comes.' I said, 'I don't mind, I'm sure he's very clean – but quite a few of the ladies when they turn up' – I used to do hair there – 'and find the door being opened by the frou-frou man wouldn't appreciate it.'

Derek: I don't think they liked him serving the coffee and biscuits.

Elizabeth: When he'd been working all night emptying the loos ... We used to visit the cruise ships that came: go on board, do a bit of shopping. I'm sure all the passengers thought we were all natives: they used to hang over the edge watching us. We all dressed up in our best outfits to go. You had to go down these steps, swing into a little boat, from that to another boat and go alongside these liners. Not the sort of thing you wanted to do with children ...

Derek: The children didn't go near the sea. Because the sea was dangerous. All of a sudden out of a calm sea you could get these enormous waves, coming rushing in. There might not have been any for weeks, but then they'd come tearing up two hundred feet or so.

Elizabeth: The children didn't go down to the beach, it was so drilled into them that they shouldn't go there on their own. I mean, they did naughty things, emptying out sumps from an old bus one time, but never on the beach. They ran round all the time – no shoes, they never wore shoes.

Derek: Just a pair of shorts. Their feet were hardened against the clinker.

Elizabeth: They found it strange when they went up on Green Mountain because everything was nice and soft. They never wore shoes, the kids.

Tony Dunne *worked on Ascension in the very early 1960s. His feelings about the island were less ecstatic.*

Coming to Ascension, the liner anchored a mile or two off. You got into a largish launch and then a hundred yards off you got into a long-boat, a rowing boat that landed at the jetty which, I suppose was about fifteen foot high. And enormous swells. You had to step pretty smartly off the stern of the boat, which was held very skilfully in place by the oarsman, onto the steps, and nip up before the next swell came and took you away. Our daughter was then about a year old – one of the boatmen took her, shouted something incomprehensible to a fellow on top of the jetty, and then hurled the child at us! Fortunately she was caught.

There were, I think, about three hundred Americans, a couple of hundred St Helena men and twenty, twenty-five English. Half a dozen St Helena men had their wives and perhaps half the English had wives. So women were in a very small minority. Sixteen out of ... five hundred or something ...

It was said that if ever you saw a bachelor on Ascension wearing Wellington boots it was time to post him. Because there were loads of shoes there and it never rained ...

Two of us looked after all the HF radio. It was mainly a cable station, a telegraph cable station but we had regular voice contact back to UK and particularly to the States, because with all these Americans they were forever making calls. I do remember the American technician at the other end being a bit surprised when he wanted me to change frequency, and I said, 'I'll just be about twenty minutes.' I got on my bicycle, rode down the other end of town, changed frequency – which in those days was heaving great coils of copper about and twiddling them and so on – and back again. 'All I do is press a button. Why does it take you twenty minutes?' I explained all this bicycling and copper heaving and so on. He obviously thought it was not at all like White Plains [headquarters of AT&T].

John Packer *spent two periods working on Ascension. He came to love the island with passion, and has left his mark in the form of the Ascension Historical (now Heritage) Society he helped found.*

The island had a peculiar feel. When I first went there [in the late 1950s], there was a notice at the entrance saying *Georgetown. Water from Green Mountain* – I didn't realise the significance of that at the time – population 185. And a week later they had to change it to 186 since I'd arrived and I was relieving somebody who hadn't yet left. I then discovered that the water indeed came from Green Mountain, and this island was an anachronism. Here were 185 people all working for the same Company, on a remote island, where the Manager was the resident magistrate – in a sense the uncrowned king of the island – and the only means of arrival and departure were the mail boats every four or six weeks. Between that, one was cut off and yet in instant contact with the rest of the world with all these cables. One knew what was happening in the world: yet leave the cable office and you stepped back into the old naval garrison, which was what the town was, a relic of the past with ancient cannons pointing out to sea to defend the island. The old naval church, the naval barrack block, all the bungalows the staff lived in had been inherited from the Royal Navy when they had pulled out from Ascension back in the 1920s.

There was this feeling of living in the past. But during that first tour the Americans arrived with their first survey parties, to restore the airstrip that had been built during World War Two and had since fallen into disrepair. That was where I had learned to drive – there was wide open space where you weren't in danger of hitting the rocks. They arrived to start the installation of their tracking sites, involved in those days in the guided missile programme. That led on to Gemini and then to Apollo.

So although the day I arrived the island was a sort of relic of the last century, within that first tour the twentieth century arrived with a vengeance. The space age.

Returning to Ascension Island after six years, John Packer discovered that although there had been substantial changes in the place, many of the old working ways lingered still.

The sense of remoteness was lessened by weekly aircraft – the airstrip was fully operational – and the sense of more people on the island, although it was still a very small population and you had only to walk half a mile and you were on your own. The contrast, even then, between some of the cable equipment that was still working (although there weren't quite so many teak boxes and bits of polished brass around) and the earth station, which was on a level with all of the American dishes. The staff at the earth station thought perhaps that they were with the latest generation of technology, while the folks down at the cable office, who also looked after the island's telephone exchange, were perhaps feeling that they weren't quite so far ahead with things.

While I was there, I helped an American start the Ascension Historical

Georgetown, the main settlement on Ascension Island

Society. The island was littered with things that had been chucked away, like an old steam-driven fire engine from the Navy days, and an old horse-drawn carriage. The horse wasn't there but the carriage still was. All these things were in danger of being pushed into the sea. We thought it was a pity if they got lost, and so we started a society – partly to provide interest for some of the youngsters on the island. We got permission to use an old Napoleonic fort to turn into a little museum. In part of the fort there was a little building right at the top to which we fitted a sliding roof and turned into a little observatory.

We used to go up there. We had found a radio receiver that dated from World War Two: it had been used by the Americans for receiving from aircraft at the airstrip, and it was still working. So we were able to tune in to a circuit between the island and one of the American tracking ships during part of the Apollo mission. What they were relaying to the ship was the voices of the astronauts. And we had this telescope trained on the Moon, and we were able to look at the craters that the astronauts were describing as they were travelling over them in the spacecraft ...

It was the first time that men had gone to the Moon – not landed, but they were orbiting it ... There is something on the moon called the Great Wall. It looks like a crack on the surface through a telescope, and we could just make it out as a faint line. They were talking about a particular crater they were going over and I was predicting they would say, any minute now, that they were coming in sight of the Great Wall. Sure enough, five minutes later, they did ... Now we're so blasé – Moon missions, Mars missions – but it was happening while we were there watching it, and our own earth station was involved in it, and our own staff. Later that evening I would be on watch at the earth station helping these circuits to go through. It gave one the most curious feeling.

John Worrall *represented a new breed, the satellite station engineer, and on Ascension he was treated accordingly. The island and its way of life were to be changed radically by the improvements in conditions that came with the new technology.*

At that time [in the 1960s] they were starting to introduce satellite communication. We'd got a contract at Cable & Wireless to build a little earth station on Ascension Island for the NASA Apollo programme. At the end of my advanced training I was selected to go on a Marconi training course at Chelmsford on satellite communication. It was exciting, because this was the forefront of technology. I went there for several weeks as part of my honeymoon! ... We were also expected to do new earth station projects at places like Hong Kong or the West Indies, and I was rather hoping it would be Hong Kong or the West Indies. Nevertheless, Ascension it was. I might have guessed that would happen – I was rather hoping I wouldn't, because Ascension isn't exactly an attractive proposition to anyone, particularly if you were a bachelor. At least I was married.

So we went off to Ascension in 1966 and spent two years there, both of us ... When you arrive on Ascension – it's like arriving on the moon. It's absolutely terrible: craters everywhere, lava, volcanoes. There's this little green mountain in the middle, and you wonder, 'Where the hell have I got to? And I've got to spend two years here!'

They built some new prefabricated bungalows particularly for the earth station project, and we were put in these brand new bungalows. New furniture, curtains, and even flush toilets, which the other residents of the island didn't have. So of course, immediately, we were very much the newcomers, getting all this special attention. It was a nice atmosphere there. There was Cable & Wireless, the BBC were there, the relay station, Civil Service, GCHQ doing their usual thing, and of course the Americans. It seemed like every little hillock in Ascension was covered in secret aerials of some sort or other. The place was bristling. It's seven miles by four, and you've never seen a place bristling with so much electronic equipment.

Ascension encompassed almost 150 years of communications, right from the very earliest submarine cables ... But we were the new boys, because we had the flush toilets and the latest satellite technology. I think what hurt most was the flush toilets, to be honest.

'Can you imagine somewhere where you can throw a cricket ball across? And you spend that much time there?' A fairly typical Company reaction to life on Cocos, this remote island was one of the most awkward places to which a man might be sent. Yet those who went there frequently seem to have enjoyed it and borne the privations with equanimity.

Keith Warren *was posted to Cocos soon after the Second World War was over. During the war, Cocos had been essential for the Allies' communications, and Pete Wolfe's experiences are recorded below (pp 133–4). Even when peace came, Cocos was a difficult place to be posted to. Supplies and boat passages were difficult, while one event brought home all too clearly the dangers of such a remote existence.*

I was called upon to assist the doc to take a chap's appendix out. At the end of the island there was a group of people employed by the Admiralty to take direction finding bearings on foreign warships, and one of them, a young chap about our age, developed appendicitis. We had a very good doctor on the island ... he was always very keen on surgery and was really I feel waiting for anything to go wrong to keep his hand in ....

The doctor knew I was able to help with these sort of things without actually falling into a faint on the floor ... The first thing the doc tried to do was to put him out with ether ... but he wouldn't go, he was thrashing about. He said, 'Some people don't go out with ether, so I'll give him a spinal injection.' He bent him over and gave him a spinal injection – I didn't like the look of that, so I went outside to get a little bit of fresh air – waited for a bit, and with the handle of his knife stroked him on the tummy and said, 'Can you feel that?' And this chap said, 'Well yes, I can, but go ahead, Doc.' 'No, we don't want any heroics, I can't cut into a muscle if you're feeling it.' What he also had was Pentathol. It still leaves you your reflexes. It put him out all right, but every time the doctor made a cut the patient's knees came up, so we had to call in somebody else to hold the knees down ... From then onwards

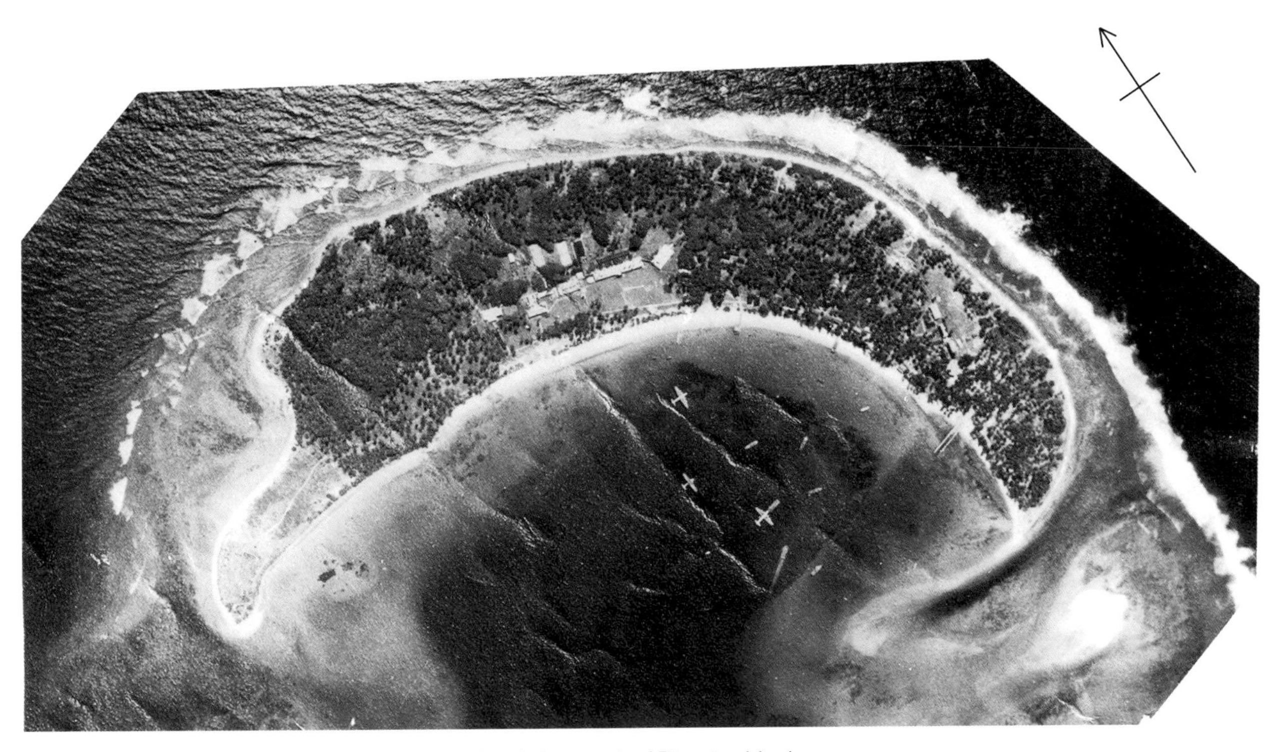

Aerial photograph of Direction Island,
the Company's base in the Cocos-Keeling Islands

it was fairly straightforward. It took him a little time to find where the appendix was, the doctor fished it out, took a look at it and said, 'It's a bit like a wet cigarette and wouldn't have lasted more than a couple of hours really' ... He allowed me just to put in one stitch, because he could see I was very interested.

It ended happily because the chap recovered without any problems, I'm pleased to say. He was a very brave lad because I wouldn't have liked to have been in his position. That was something which has stayed in my memory as you can well imagine, and I am sure it stayed in his too.

John Nash *was stationed on the island a short time later. He took part – as every member of staff did at some time during their stay on Cocos – in one of its best-known ceremonies.*

We had a boat every six months – that was it. You got a boat to Singapore called the *Islander* which went down through the Cinnabar Straits and then out across the Indian Ocean. Its real function was to collect phosphates from an island called Christmas Island ... The boat was used for supplies for Cable & Wireless, and also supplies for Clunies Ross. It would also bring new staff and take away staff. And it would also load copra from John Clunies Ross's estate, then go back to Christmas Island and then Singapore.

You accepted life there. It was of course idyllic from the point of view of swimming or sailing and that sort of thing. And then the duties continued ...

It didn't *seem* a strange life. I don't know why not.

There was one little ceremony we had. The Orient Line ship went from the King Colombo in Perth and it used to come quite close to Cocos. Now and then they would radio when they were on their way and they'd say, 'We'll drop a barrel.' This became quite a famous thing. The staff off-duty would get in a boat, we'd sail outside the lagoon a mile or so and the ship would appear: a very large liner. We'd have a tin can filled with our mail, suitably franked Tin Can Mail. The ship would throw a barrel over the stern, a barrel with fresh butter and stuff like that. And we'd almost heave to and pick up this barrel. I don't think we heaved it aboard because it was too heavy, but we attached it to the boat. We'd tie our tin can onto a rope, and they'd take our mail, and we'd go back with a barrel of fresh food.

That started before the war, that tradition, and was kept up until the Company ceased operation there – or until they no longer had passenger ships. It was quite a sight. You'd be standing on this boat and there'd be this huge ship with the rails lined with these gorgeous-looking women.

Derek Moore *was sent at his own request to Cocos in the course of his first tour of duty in the early 1950s.*

I was a technician in the cable office [at Colombo]. For a couple of years I was posted to the Cocos-Keeling Islands – because I asked to go there. Everyone thought I was totally mad, but I wanted to experience what it was like to live on a remote desert island.

Direction Island. A mile and a half long, two hundred yards wide, six feet above sea level, and five hundred miles from anywhere ... We had one near pass of a cyclone when I was there. The buildings, that were made of corrugated iron and wood, were raised on steel girders five or six feet above the island. When there was a full storm warning, big cables were put over the roof to anchor blocks to hold them all down, so the storm wouldn't blow them away and the sea could go underneath. We never had one quite as bad as that.

There was very little to do really. We used to sail a lot. Play tennis. Run round the island. If there was any drink we'd drink it – not always the case. I was made mess caterer, so at the age of 21 I had to order all the food and drink six months in advance. If the ship was late you ran out of everything. When on one occasion it was late for nearly two months we lived on corned beef and rice most of the time.

ORION

Going out for supplies from a passing ship at Cocos (left),
and supplies successfully received!

Maurice Bane *was also stationed on Cocos in the early part of the 1950s, when it was a three-monthly ship's visit. These men were among the last of the Company personnel to be sent to Cocos before it was handed over to Australia.*

The first impact of Cocos: it's covered in palm trees. The highest point on the whole of the island is only about 12 or 15 feet and I remember thinking, Gosh, if there's a tidal wave this whole lot will disappear. We steamed into this lagoon and it was very beautiful, a very calm day, and the colours – greens, blues, dark blues, coral shining through at various places ... We anchored, and a boat came alongside. All these characters came clambering on board. This was the staff, and what a ragged-looking scruffy bunch they were. Most of them barefooted, holes in their shorts, tattered shirts, long hair, looked like a bunch of castaways, all of course as brown as berries, some of them no shirts at all. [The new manager being posted there] looked at them and said to me, 'Oh dear, looks like we're going to have to straighten this lot out.'

When Maurice Bane left for Singapore, eighteen months later, he had had an idyllic time until a boating tragedy marred the island's tranquillity.

We had to cross the road and I was scared stiff, all these cars whizzing up and down the road. They were probably only doing about 20 miles an hour but to me ... Think about it: a whole year, probably a bit more, no noise except the wind in the palms, the surf on the reef, occasional voices in the distance – and suddenly the hurly burly of Singapore.

CHAPTER FOUR

War

When Hong Kong was liberated from the Japanese at the end of the Second World War, it was one of the happiest days of my life. We just rode around on our bicycles, throwing firecrackers. And nobody wanted to stop us.

Fung Hak Ming

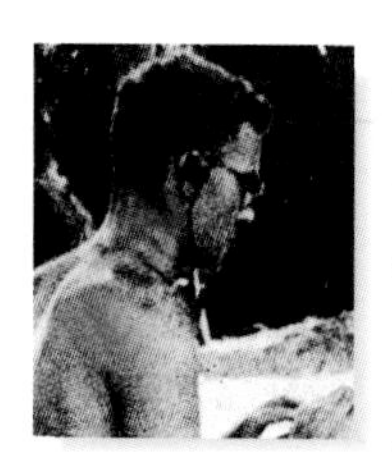

If truth is the first casualty of war, communications must often run it a close second. In many areas of conflict there has been specialist back-up provided by the telecommunications companies. Cable & Wireless's special and distinctive contribution to the Second World War is well known and justly celebrated: keeping the lines of communication open through its paramilitary arm TELCOM, following the troops in the theatres of war, maintaining the cables that came into Britain at Porthcurno, and participation in what was intended to be the last push in the war against Japan but swiftly became a liberation force. The effects of war were felt throughout the Company and around the globe. Rather less well known is Cable & Wireless's contribution in other areas of conflict. In subsequent wars, in the Arab–Israeli conflicts, in Korea (when TELCOM was still operational) and in Vietnam, Cable & Wireless maintained an important presence.

Keith Warren *joined Cable & Wireless in 1943. He had been in the Royal Naval Volunteer Reserve, waiting to be called up for war duty, but chose instead to have a telecommunications training.*

Cable & Wireless in those days was run by Sir Edward Wilshaw, and his attitude was that the war was being fought by the Army, Navy, Air Force, and Cable & Wireless. It has to be said that virtually all of the Empire communications were in the hands of Cable & Wireless.

Pete Wolfe *was recruited just before the Second World War, and was stationed in a number of places to help keep the channel of communications open and flowing. One stretch of his wartime experience was spent on the remote Cocos-Keeling Islands in the Indian Ocean.*

If you can imagine it, a coral atoll group. The island we were on was about a quarter of a mile long, 150 yards or so wide and the highest point above sea level was six feet. When we dug our trenches we were into water. So when we went in the trenches when the Japanese bombers came over, we were up to our waists in water. But that was better than being on the surface.

The reconnaissance used to come over every month. After Singapore fell, they had shelled the island to destroy the cable station. But they only damaged it, and hit the Chinese quarters. The Japanese gave out that they'd destroyed the station. So we allowed all the defences to go to rack and ruin, and we weren't allowed to put any washing out or appear during the day. We had six dogs on the island, and they were our air-raid warning. They could hear the Japanese plane long before we could (because of the noise of the surf breaking on the reef round the island). So as soon as my dog got up from under my desk in the office and went under the building, which was on stilts, we rang the alarm bell. Two minutes later the Japanese plane would come over and we were all hidden.

Then in 1944 the Japanese decided that we *were* still there because we still had communication with Australia. This Japanese bomber came over, strafed Home Island where the Malays lived and then came across the lagoon at 200 feet. We were in a trench at the top of the beach, about ten of us. We saw this plane coming across and we saw the bomb leave it, heading straight for us. So we ducked down and it actually landed about, what, about twenty feet away. And showered us with salt water and sand. Unhurt ...

When I went down there, there were five Cable & Wireless men, two Australian Air Force men doing weather reports which we sent by cable, two Americans communicating with agents in Sumatra and also sending their stuff back to Ceylon via us, fifty African troops and sixty Navy chaps doing

Japanese radio interception. The Japanese never kept radio silence and these Navy blokes did Japanese Morse, which they then coded and handed to us. We sent it by cable to Ceylon and other places, with all the intelligence that the Japanese were giving away by transmitting by radio. So we were quite snowed under with work.

After this Japanese bomber came over they decided we needed some defences so they sent a hundred Marines down and they ringed the island with Oerlikons and God-knows-what. They arrived on the Saturday, spent a week building emplacements, but didn't have a single gun ready for action. A Japanese plane came over, took one look – 'Ah! Gun emplacements' – went up to 10,000 feet, pushed off, and never came back. So the Marines spent three months practising for something that never happened. Then in January 1945 I went back to Ceylon with the Marines and they were relieved by an Indian detachment of troops.

John Rippengal *qualified from Company training towards the end of the war, and was put into uniform in the special TELCOM unit. The ultimate intention was to support the Allied push into Japanese-held Asia, and considerable numbers of Company employees were appointed to TELCOM units. Their presence was first felt in the North Africa campaigns, and subsequently men like John Rippengal were posted into Asia. But first, he had to get out there ...*

The German war was still on, the U-boat campaign was in its last desperate throes, and pretty vicious, so it was quite an interesting method of getting on the ship. First of all, you were told to go home and stay by the phone, not to do anything. You weren't told where you were going, what you were going to do, nothing. After a week I got a phone call and they said, 'Right, you go to Euston, you get on such and such a train, go to Liverpool.' It was all secret you know. At Liverpool we were met and carted off to a big Gothic hotel. We stayed there, just told to stay there, we were there three or four days ...

One morning they said, 'OK, come on,' and we got on a lighter and got on board ship and that was a shock: it was a Dutch ship, with Dutch officers, the seamen were Brits. It had come over when Holland had fallen, the *Stuyvesant.* At the end of the war, 1945, the food was bloody awful, terribly restricted; once we got on this ship, it was like a ship at any time. All ships have masses of luxurious food, and the cook on this ship was excellent, there were a lot of passengers on it, and we had any amount of food, things we'd never seen. Great big hams, rounds of beef, real eggs instead of dried ones. Incredible. A very pleasant ship, about a hundred passengers, 13,000 tons. We set off that night and God knows where we went. It was all dark, no lights, we joined up with a convoy, frigates and destroyers dashing up and down, and we had quite a few submarine warnings. They were dropping depth charges for the next three or four nights until we cleared the Atlantic lanes. Passengers had to do so many hours of deck watch to watch for submarines and that sort of thing.

Being a convoy, we went at the speed of the slowest ship, so we were at sea for about two and a half weeks. We didn't know where we were, nobody told us and it was just nothing but sea all round. I think we must have been off Gibraltar when most of the convoy disappeared off to the left and we were left on our own and we went to our full 13 knots and went to Takoradi in West Africa. We had £10 each when we got on board, that's all we were allowed. Can you imagine, for nearly a month's journey. We had to find our way from Takoradi to Accra where the [Company's] office was, but fortunately we found a policeman on the same ship, who took us down ...

We were then told to get to the airport one night at 11 o'clock and we got into a Liberator bomber and flew to Ascension which is where we were aiming for. Ascension Island. We were feeling pretty bruised and battered now, having arrived from Takoradi to Accra in the back of a policeman's lorry ... I'd never flown in an aeroplane before, one didn't then. It was a regular RAF run twice a week with supplies and things. We arrived in Ascension and of course, this was tremendously enjoyable. I was 20, just coming up to 21, and it was a marvellous thing to be able to do, a real adventure. It was wonderful.

SEEING IS BELIEVING

No longer need imagination conjure visions of other lands – to-day one half of the world can see how the other half lives ! • By means of the Phototelegraph Transmitter, phototelegrams can be flashed across the world. • On the other side the Phototelegraph Receiver reproduces the identical pictures, ready for publication. • Cable and Wireless are opening more Phototelegraph circuits as equipment becomes available. • When peace returns the free nations of the world will see and share events and interests of everyday life as they have shared the effort and suffering of war.

SEND YOUR PHOTOS 'VIA IMPERIAL'

CABLE AND WIRELESS LIMITED • ELECTRA HOUSE • VICTORIA EMBANKMENT • LONDON • W.C.2

A great way to spend your time – and Ascension was interesting, this weird lunar landscape and these piles of cinders that had fallen down.

We left Ascension on a glider-towing Dakota being delivered, a new aeroplane. Which was quite an adventure: no seats on the aeroplane, just lots of crates of cargo, two huge great extra fuel tanks on board, just behind the cockpit. No co-pilot, one pilot, one navigator, one radio operator. They were RAF transport command: first of all they refused to take us, I remember that. We went very early having had a party late as a farewell. We spoke to a Major somebody in the US Air Force, and he said to us, 'Where do you want to go?' We said Colombo. He said, 'Oh yeah,' but he looked a bit blank, so we said Ceylon, and he said, 'Oh yeah. Oh shit, do you want to go east or west from here?'

Anyway, we took off on this thing. The crew didn't want to take us, they said they were over-loaded – they were very shaky, they had a hangover I think. I sat in the co-pilot's seat, there were no other seats, and my colleague Brian Suart sat on the floor. I always remember going to sleep because I was so bloody tired, and waking up an hour or two later and finding myself alone – well, I thought I was alone – in the cockpit, in this aeroplane over the South Atlantic, with nothing all around. I thought, 'My God, they've all bailed out and left me alone.' But no, they were all sitting in the fuselage behind some crates, playing cards and drinking whisky. My colleague and the three crew – and the final straw, every fifteen minutes the navigator, who had a Rolex on each wrist, took a bubble sextant shot through a little astrodome. In the DC3s because there were no radio aids in those days, they didn't know where the hell they were except by astro-navigation, and they really needed to know how much longitude they were making otherwise we might never have got anywhere. You didn't know what the wind was or anything. He was doing this! The other thing they were terribly worried about was fuel. The main auxiliary tanks were on gauges, but the in-board tanks had no gauge. The only way they could tell if there was any fuel was with a dipstick. Can you imagine? There was this navigator and he had the top of the tank open, with a dipstick, and he had a cigarette. It was all great fun.

We were going to Colombo. We'd been told to go urgently because we

The Company celebrating the release of prisoners of war in 1945

were going to join the Zipper operation [to liberate South-East Asia]. We went down from Accra, then BOAC to Lagos, there a few days, then we caught another Dakota to Cairo, through Khartoum. That's an interesting trip, all through the desert: northern Nigeria, Chad, Sudan. Overnight in Khartoum and up to Cairo ... By now, both of us had a most incredible dysentery! We got on a flying boat, the old Empire Class flying boat, taking two days to Karachi where we were marooned because the airport was flooded. We were there about eight days, still suffering. We both finally arrived, once again on an RAF Dakota, from Karachi to Colombo ...

Having recovered from that we spent a month installing a radio station in an infantry landing craft, the Press Ship. We set sail on that, went from Colombo to Trincomalee to join up with the fleet which was going to be the Zipper operation. We were going to land this thing in Malaya, somewhere on the Malayan coast.

This was July. VE [Victory in Europe] happened around my 21st birthday. We celebrated it the end of May, yes, and I remember a big party in Ascension and a dance at which everybody got very drunk, which wasn't difficult or expensive. The Japanese war was still on, but as we set sail they dropped the atom bombs and so instead of going to the beaches, we went straight down to Singapore. We got in this enormous convoy ... An enormous fleet of warships, hospital ships, supply ships, incredible. We went across the Bay of Bengal, and I don't know whether you've seen one of these landing crafts, infantry, large, they're about a hundred tons and very narrow and draw about two feet. A most dreadful thing to travel across the Bay of Bengal in: monsoon blowing, everybody was sick. It took ten days to get across, and until we got around the northern end of Sumatra, nine days, it was pretty rough. But from there on it was like a mill pond down the Straits of Malacca.

We went into Singapore with this incredible line of ships which went miles and miles in all directions, as far as you could see, and when we arrived, anchored off Telok Ayer, the Japanese had told everybody to stay in. Not a soul to be seen. If you can imagine, a Chinese city with nobody about ... We dropped anchor about 1 o'clock, lunch time, and it wasn't until 5 o'clock that two entrepreneurs came out with some bananas they wanted to sell. The next day we went ashore. The Japanese were walking about, the officers still had their swords on, hadn't been rounded up. We were the first troops there.

And the streets were knee-deep in money. Bank notes.

The British arrangement was pretty good. They'd got the old notes into the banks on Day One, and they made an announcement: Japanese money was finished. Already it had inflated to millions, so it was virtually useless anyhow. 'The old money is back in circulation, you can come and get it.' Everybody as a gesture of derision to the Japanese had thrown their money out of the window; it was all lying around the streets.

The ship in fact was the only means of communication for all the British forces for the first two weeks ... All the foreign correspondents were supposed to travel with us. They took one look at the ship and said, No way. They went on the military ship, but we carried all the military and civilian [communications] traffic out of there. We opened up the office then [in Singapore] and apart from the transmitter that was on the ship, we moved receivers and telegraph equipment into the old building and just connected it with lines to the ship, which was by then tied alongside.

The late **Brian Suart** *was John Rippengal's companion for a considerable part of the time in TELCOM before the pair went their separate ways into high-level careers with Cable & Wireless.*

During the war, Cable & Wireless had quite a number of mobile radio stations, all in trucks, and operating on various fronts providing service for the pressmen. But someone had the bright idea of putting one on a ship. This was the Press Ship that my friend and I helped to install. And then we sailed as the Assistant Engineers on it in the reoccupation of Malaya, Operation Zipper.

This was after the European war had ended, and the Far East war was still going on.

TELCOM personnel camping in the condemned cells in immediate post-war Jakarta

We were destined to go up the beach at Port Dixon with the invading troops; but before we got to Penang the Japanese surrendered and we sailed down the Straits of Malacca, calmly into Singapore harbour, and tied up very close to the Cable & Wireless office there. And did what we were sent to do, which was to provide a service for the pressmen, and of course rapidly got stuck into the business of resuming communications, restoring cables which had been interrupted, and relaying ... I stayed nearly four years, working in both Singapore and Jurong where we built a transmitting station.

Colin Stubbs *was recruited from his native New Zealand as part of the Australasian contingent for TELCOM.*

The major part of our time was spent in Jakarta, we were in the old Japanese Campti Jail on the Boulevard and split up to live in the condemned cells. Two in a cell, quite roomy, pretty bare, and we worked pretty hard. At one stage I went down to Bali to open up a press link, administration link for the Bali invasion you might call it. That was a total fiasco: we got there, there wasn't one press correspondent, we never exchanged one second of communication at all, and that was it, we just went there, put up our aerials, got our transmitter going, didn't receive a thing, then we joined the press ship which came down.

Paul Foster *trained to be an operator in wartime in his native Barbados, together with his friend Arthur Farmer.*

We were both 17 years old, around that age. By that time we had qualified and went on to the circuit, which was on the army wireless station. You were a ship watch station, and during the war the ships had to maintain radio silence. The only time they came up was if they either saw a submarine or were torpedoed and they had enough time to say something. Here we were, two 17-year-olds in a very responsible position, because when we did get any of these XXXs or SSSs as they became, high priority stuff, we had to control this thing. There we were in full command of the situation: everybody had to keep quiet while we communicated with the ship. We then had to rush messages off to Trinidad and Puerto Rico. Trinidad had a Fleet Air Arm, so did Puerto Rico.

Then there was the day war came to Barbados: 21 September 1942.

I was playing tennis and looked towards the sea. There were buildings in front of us and they had a net across the harbour and ships would come in – sort of sneak in and get inside – and there were at least two ships in. A German sub had sneaked up and pumped about four torpedoes through this net before he was able to get one inside, which hit a Canadian National steamship called the *Cornwallis*. We heard all this noise, so my immediate reaction was I would go to the wireless station because they'd know what was happening, and I did. The population surged towards Bridgetown when they heard all this noise – and when they found out what it was there was a mass evacuation. I was caught in the middle of it, so I just stayed and saw it out with the operator on duty at the time. The operator who was present when it happened closed the station and left, because he was not sure what was going to happen. This other more senior operator came to see what was happening, and he opened it up and took over.

He would let Trinidad and Puerto Rico know. Then about two hours later some old flying boat or something came over Bridgetown. Everybody shouted, 'Hooray, we're saved.' It circled around a while. By that time the U-boat had gone. The story was eventually, the next year, it got sunk in the Bay of Biscay and it and its crew were lost. There were a lot of interesting stories during the war about U-boats in St Lucia; they came in and hid up in the inlets where [Admirals] Hood and Rodney used to do the same thing against the French ...

The TELCOM system was maintained until after cessation of hostilities in the Korean War. The press and military communications lines had been kept open through the crisis in Palestine as the state of Israel was born amid Arab–Jewish conflict. **Albert Lorens** *was born in what had been Palestine, a British Mandate, but in 1949 was to find himself an employee of Cable & Wireless in the new state of Israel. On either side of that date he was in the midst of terrorism and strife.*

I had to wait five years to get my British passport. The passport I had before was identical, it looked the same, but it was issued in Palestine and the Israeli government were so anti-British they clipped the end of it so that it was useless ... I left on temporary documents that said, 'Already stateless because issued in Israel'. I didn't want to be Israeli, and Palestine did not exist any more. Overnight. You are in one area and the country changes. One day you are in Palestine, the next day you are in Israel. It doesn't happen to many people like that.

That was a dangerous place. The manager in Haifa sent a message to Jaffa [where I was working] and said to the F1 staff and myself to come back to Haifa. 'Pack and come back, take a taxi and come back.' But we couldn't come back the normal way. We had to go through Nablus, which was a hundred per cent Muslim. In those days people disappeared and that was it. That really worried me. So we packed everything and we found a driver with a taxi. Then one of the Muslim leaders asked if he could come back with us to Haifa. I said, 'No, we want a taxi on our own.' But then I told my colleague, 'We'd better take him with us, since we're not going through the normal route, we're going through Nablus.' He sat next to the driver and indeed he was very useful. There was a road block in Nablus, there was a long discussion with the chap there and probably he convinced them everything was OK, so we carried on to Haifa. And the driver said: 'There's one more place where there are snipers, nearer to Haifa. If we get through there we'll be OK.' We got through OK. So we made it.

That would be 1947, or early 1948. An explosion then took place in Haifa: the office was shattered and we had to do quick work to keep the communication going.

I was on duty. I was supposed to leave at 4 o'clock and to be relieved by one of the foreign staff, one of the British staff. He phoned me, he said not

Getting the message through: Cable & Wireless's wartime advertising underlined its long heritage

COMMUNICATIONS

2.—WHEN RUNNERS BROUGHT THE NEWS

WHEN wars were waged in days of old, the prowess of runners might turn the scales of battle. Slight of stature, with the endurance born of long training, these athletic 'aces'—human lines of communication—sometimes held the fate of Empires in their hands.

Wings of Victory

When reinforcements were desperately wanted, or after a victory, runners were chosen to carry the news to the capital. Climbing mountains, fording rivers, they risked death to bring home the tidings. A famous Grecian runner, after an epic run of over twenty-two miles, died on the outskirts of Athens—the message of the great victory at Marathon on his lips. He had given his life to get the message through.

And Now—

To-day, when secret messages still turn the tide of battle, their transmission is a matter of seconds. Time and space have been beaten by science, harnessed in the service of mankind by the pioneers and promoters of cable and wireless communication. In the affairs of peace, as of war, that public utility service known as Cable and Wireless Ltd., flashing endless waves of messages '*via* Imperial' over routes covering more than twelve times the earth's circumference, plays a vital and ever-growing part.

CABLE AND WIRELESS LTD

The only British owned and operated Overseas Telegraph Company in this country

November 17 1941 PUNCH ALMANACK FOR 1942 ix

COMMUNICATIONS

THE LANGUAGE OF FLAGS

THE METHOD of sending messages by flag-waving is well known to soldiers, sailors, and boy scouts. Long before the invention of wireless the flags of England's coastguard stations were often to be seen exchanging semaphore messages with ships at sea. From hill-top to hill-top soldiers used flags to pass on vital orders.

Nelson's Broadcast

By a Naval system of flag-hoists of very ancient origin—greatly developed in recent times—Lord Nelson's immortal message was broadcast to his fleet at Trafalgar. Up to the masthead ran that famous call to duty, "England Expects"—a call that was again sent out to British men-of-war, and again as nobly answered, in the battle of the River Plate.

186,000 Miles a Second

Flags still play their picturesque part for short-distance communication. But for long distances we rely to-day on the lightning speed of messages sent under the sea and through the air. Thanks to the world-wide services developed by Cable and Wireless Ltd., messages—'*via* Imperial'—can cross the globe in a flash, and at remarkably inexpensive rates. Such facilities have opened a new era of social and economic progress; they have helped to establish a cohesion of Empire whose strength must always lie in its power of swift and easy contact.

CABLE AND WIRELESS LTD

The only British owned and operated Overseas Telegraph Company in this country

to worry, not to wait for him, to go home and he would be coming a bit later. I said OK. But before my duty ended something went wrong with the equipment so I couldn't leave it, I would be in real trouble just leaving it. So I fixed that and then by the time I finished he arrived. He said, 'Why did you wait?' I said I had no choice, I had to fix a piece of the equipment. I got on my motor bike, went home. As soon as I got home, [there was] a big explosion. I looked back and dust was in the air somewhere in town. I thought, 'Just another explosion.' I ignored it. The following day in the morning a messenger came, and said, 'Go to the office right away, they want you.'

The window frame was ripped off, the battery room acid was all over the place, and we had to do quick work. Just fifteen minutes after I left, the explosion had happened. Luckily only one or two were slightly injured, probably flying glass or something like that. But no serious injuries at all. The target was the police headquarters next door. They drove one of those armoured cars into the headquarters of the post office – we were on the fourth floor in the post office, we had half of their floor. The post office was here [on one side] and the police headquarters there [on the other] and the car went between the two and stayed there. The back axle – the following day we saw the back axle [had landed] somewhere else ...

Again, when I reached Tel Aviv communication was interrupted and they said there was a small explosion ... That was just another one of many. If it was not the Jews placing bombs, it would be the Arabs. It was all the time changing. If not Jews against Arabs, then Jews against the government or the Arabs against the government. It was going on all the time.

But, after that, leaving Haifa, leaving Palestine, with all that trouble, Algiers was the next place. This time the French [were the targets]. There I missed being blown to pieces by just fifteen minutes. I was going to my favourite place and it was all in pieces, everything shattered. That place was a milk bar, I'd never seen anything like it, really beautiful, all painted mirrors and glass. I thought, 'It seems wherever I go, I walk into it.' That is, until I came to England.

Cable & Wireless personnel with Palestinians who were caught in the struggle to found Israel in 1948

John Rippengal *whose wartime experiences in TELCOM were recounted above, was the Manager of International Relations and Deputy General Manager of the Hong Kong branch in the 1960s. He re-entered the theatres of war with a more commercial eye.*

One of the best things we ever did, and in fact made a huge difference to the Company's profitability – and even more to the cash flow – was the setting up of the Vietnamese thing. Especially the 'GI Call Home' programme ...

One day, it must have been 1965, an American came to my office in Mercury House [Hong Kong]. His name was Bob Corbridge, from AT&T, ex-submariner during the war. He asked if we could help him, he had a problem with some minor electronic thing. We had a Chinese technical wizard who came in, and he told him what he wanted. I said have a cup of coffee, we had the coffee; by the time we'd finished the coffee the guy brought it back and it was already made. And he was absolutely flabbergasted. Corbridge was going on to Vietnam because they were under tremendous pressure about the GIs being able to call home. The only way they could call home was on the MARS network, the Military Amateur Radio System. That was useless. So I felt quite interested in this ...

Picking the story up, **John Bragg** *became something of a local legend in Cable & Wireless, not least because of his experiences amidst the craziness of the Vietnam War. He left the Company to live in Australia after experience in most areas of fighting in South-East Asia.*

I was at the Polo Club in Manila and we'd had a few beers and I was asked, 'Would you like to volunteer to go to Vietnam?' They couldn't get anybody else to go to Vietnam so that's where I went. They gave me a choice in the morning – they said, 'You know you volunteered to go to Vietnam' – but you couldn't very well back down once you'd ... I went to Vietnam, for the next five years, and it was very pleasant.

GIs returning from the front line in Vietnam. The Call Home programme enabled them to contact family and friends in the USA with ease

I went through Hong Kong and arrived in Vietnam on 8 February 1966. I was assured by John Eades [from Hong Kong] that he'd got the Australian Embassy in Saigon to have a hotel for me. Of course, when I got there the Australian Embassy didn't even know me and there were no hotels to be had, so the first night was spent in a shack in the back of a builder's yard. I had two huge great pieces of equipment to be installed, so the following day I secured myself a hotel room at great expense off some Americans down there who wanted better communications, and from there on I didn't look back ...

[Cable & Wireless] wanted to develop Hong Kong into more of a regional focus, so Vietnam was one of the new sort of places to start. As well as Vietnam we opened up Cambodia, Laos, Thailand, as far as Nepal. We introduced telex, and a telephone service of course, and made quite a bit of money. There was a Call Home programme: we ran twenty circuits. To this day and age twenty circuits doesn't sound much. From the USO clubs around Vietnam, hubbed through the USO downtown Saigon, back to Hong Kong on HF radio, and back to the States on satellite and cable. We ran some for the Australian forces as well. GIs used any USO club where we had a phone. All they had to do was to hit the zero button on the telephone and they got the Oakland AT&T operator. All calls were placed collect, so the revenue was generated in the States; it came through Hong Kong and we credited Vietnam ...

Vietnam – fantastic there for bachelors ... Occasional rockets came in, but you didn't see really too much of that. It wasn't really dangerous. We had one rocket land ... I had a flat there and I was showing [visitors] how we played down there, and I was pulling the pin out of a flare grenade – and chipped my tooth doing it, and bent the pin. But anyway, I finally got it out and tossed it on the roof and it landed on the railway station next door ... So we got out of there in a hurry. But those were the sort of crazy things you did. On Christmas Eve you used to stand on top of the building and shoot your gun off in all directions. The air was filled with tracer bullets – if you could get them. Yes, mad, totally mad ... As I say there were that many bachelors, that way of living, almost cowboyish for want of a better word.

John Bragg, pictured right, 'our man in Vietnam'

As a footnote, **Ian Corrall** *who had a particularly varied career in many different and difficult parts of the world for Cable & Wireless, was working in Yemen in the 1980s.*

We were just getting relaxed in Sana'a. The President of Yemen had lasted two years, which was longer than any president had lasted since the original coup. One was blown up by a briefcase bomb: a diplomat came up from his South Yemen office, opened his briefcase up and it just exploded. He didn't know the bomb was there, but it killed him and the President. So people were beginning to relax a bit. Then about 11 o'clock one night we started to hear this shooting, and I thought, 'Oh dear, here we go again.' I had the ground floor flat, so I went up to the supply officer's flat, and he said, 'I'm up here.' He was up on the roof watching, and you could see the tracer bullets and so on.

And it was an eclipse of the moon: according to local folklore there's this beast that swallows the moon, they were lighting all these fires and shooting to scare this thing off. It wasn't war after all.

CHAPTER FIVE

Out with the old – New technology, new ways

You could always break the ice by just telling them about Cable & Wireless. What we were trying to do was a bit different, and we could get people's imagination with it.

John Slaughter

Until the 1960s, Cable & Wireless's international system was firmly based upon the old tried-and-tested technologies associated with submarine telegraph cables, alongside somewhat newer radio-based systems. To many it had seemed that the old telegraph-based world would carry on more or less forever. But the radio side was developing apace, and was to become ever more inventive in improving communications; the very first satellites had been launched into orbit; there was pressure to get the old cables – some of which had been laid down in the 1870s – to work more efficiently. Meanwhile, the geopolitical realities in which Cable & Wireless had operated were changing very swiftly. The 'wind of change' that blew through the Commonwealth swept away many of the old colonial vestiges in Cable & Wireless: as former colonies became independent nations, so some at least wanted to forge their own communications identity, either in partnership with Cable & Wireless or by going it alone. In South America, where the old Western Telegraph Company had long been an important telecommunications player, franchises were not being renewed and political instability compounded the problems.

In order to survive in the new world order, Cable & Wireless had to find new business. To some extent, having changed so little for so long, it had to learn how *to find that new business. Some was in new parts of the world, some expansion in existing territories. The opportunities that presented themselves were frequently removed from the traditional core business, some in telecommunications, such as telephone systems, and some in hitherto unrelated activities – construction, broadcasting, services. By the 1970s much more contract work was being undertaken for third parties. Large-scale capital investment, in new forms of cable, in satellite and radio technology, entailed the forging of new international alliances.*

Necessarily, the 'traditional' Company existence, with large numbers of expatriate F1 staff living for lengthy terms abroad, withered, and eventually died. It was a new world: in just as many ways as exciting as the former way of life, but with rather greater uncertainty and perhaps something less of a single sense of purpose. At the end of these decades of change came the most momentous change of all: Cable & Wireless was the first of the big, landmark privatisations undertaken by the Conservative government elected in 1979.

CHANGE IN TELECOMMUNICATIONS

The days of the submarine telegraph cables were clearly numbered by the start of the 1960s. There were various attempts to improve the capability of the old cables, particularly through the development of new 'five unit' codes to replace the old Morse-type cable code, but these were only delaying the inevitable. Many cable links had already been replaced by radio links, new forms of radio transmission were being developed, and the beginnings of satellite transmission and receiving were in train. Submarine cables were to acquire a whole new lease of life with the development of coaxial cables, able to carry far greater amounts of information and making telephone transmission possible on a hitherto undreamed scale. The pace and direction of technological change were to be the dominant features of the 1960s and 1970s.

Howard Kleyn, *who had joined Cable & Wireless in 1950, and retired having helped launch Mercury in the early and mid-1980s, takes a wry look here at the technological changes that the forms of telecommunications the Company uses have undergone over those years.*

When I started, the customer was expected to come into an office and perhaps write his telegram on a piece of paper with a pencil. Or possibly, if he was very sophisticated, type it. The clerk would then count up

the words, charge him so much money, and it was then sucked into the system and was prepared for transmission by the Company's own operators. Although the standard was pretty high and the traffic was largely error-free, such errors as did occur principally came in through the preparation of the traffic for transmission, rather than the actual transmission or the machinery which handled it.

We then had the advent of telex where the customer was now operating the teleprinter, so he was responsible for sending the traffic and if there were errors they were due to him rather than to the Company – which was a great advantage as far as we were concerned ...

The customer now employs the technique known as facsimile, where again he prepares the traffic and he himself is responsible for transmitting it to the other end over the public switched telephone network. So now carriers such as Cable & Wireless have achieved, no doubt, their heart's desire – in other words, they no longer could be blamed for anything at all. All they have to do is to make sure that the links and switches are there and operating correctly without error. Which is rather easier.

Ted Amor *earned a reputation as a technical fixer, and had been one of those entrusted with the task in the mid-1950s of converting the submarine telegraph cables to new ways of working. A few men, a few tools, and an ocean to cover.*

In Head Office, they said, 'Right, we've decided to go ahead with the conversion of the system from cable code to five unit. So go into Smale House, the engineering development department, please, and familiarise yourself with the equipment. You've got two weeks' – it was like that, brand new stuff – 'and then you're going to put the pilot chain in.' And the pilot chain ran from Zanzibar to Port Louis, Seychelles, Mauritius on to Cocos. I went home to explain this to my wife ... We started off and, 'Oh, you also have to look at Dar-es-Salaam. And Nairobi.' They were all going five unit away from cable code. So we started this East African–Indian Ocean tour.

Going round explaining the new equipment and holding lectures for the staff, installing it, getting it running, running cable code and regenerator side by side, cable code and five unit side by side ... And we got it going. It was the first. A one-off.

Albert Lorens *was present when one of the old telegraph cables was finally abandoned. This scene was repeated around the world as cables, some of which had lasted for a century, went out of commission. The telegraph cables at Porthcurno itself ceased functioning in 1970.*

The last cable to Seychelles was from Colombo and it wasn't used. It was tested now and then just to make sure the cable was still OK. The equipment wasn't in good working order, so I refurbished the equipment only for closing down. The last communication exchanged was about closing the station. We celebrated at midnight. Colombo and we at the same time exchanged last messages, had some champagne, and that was the end of the Colombo station's cable.

However, I don't think people were sad when cable went. It's a matter of efficiency; the radio took over and then, in the case of Seychelles, they put an earth station there and that was very efficient. And the little radio which hardly worked properly, that too was replaced by communication through satellite. Now, that was *very* satisfactory.

Captain **Noel Smith** *formerly commanded a number of the Company's fleet of cable ships. He now lives in Chichester, still close to the sea that was his working passion for forty years. Having laid and repaired telegraph cables in almost all parts of the world, he was among the first to supervise the laying of the new coaxial cables. He describes here some of the changes that were already apparent in the early 1960s in one of Cable & Wireless's traditional heartlands, the Red Sea stations. Sometimes there were not even ceremonies to mark the demise of the cables.*

We went into Port Sudan. I had to wait 24 hours or more to get in there because it was full up with Russian ships discharging concrete – they were discharging enough concrete to build half a dozen dams. This was quite common in those days: you'd go to these foreign places, and the Russians were shipping concrete all over the place. Then we went to Aden. There was still a cable station in Aden ... While I was there, I was told to go and inspect Perim, which is a little island down the bottom of the Red Sea, which used to be a coaling port and also a Lloyd's signal station. I asked in Aden, 'Who's in charge in Perim?', and although it's just along the coast, nobody in Aden knew anything about it. They didn't know what was there or what. The signal station had been abandoned, there seemed to be nobody working there, but I was told to go so I took the ship round there. I didn't know the harbour, so I hove to outside and put the motor launch in, with the cable engineer and the chief officer, to see what the cable station was like. They found one man ashore – not just in the cable station, on the whole island there was one old fisherman there. The cable station: there was nothing of it, it had disappeared. Yet this had only happened in a short time. I remember when Perim used to be a signal station, and there was a salvage in there and piles of coal, but now it was absolutely deserted.

John Davenport *saw in the course of his career cable and wireless switch places constantly in the struggle for supremacy between the two types of system. The swing has carried on right through to the present day.*

All that polished mahogany and lacquered brass of the cable system – it didn't have long to go, did it? All the wireless stuff was dull grey paint and, with the benefit of hindsight, it was not difficult to decide which one was going to win. But having said that, it's always been of interest to me that we went through a phase shortly after my training where submarine cable telegraphy was clearly on the out, wireless was rising rapidly to the top and everybody said, 'Cable engineering is finished.' And the next thing you know,

John Davenport surveying Jehel Camp tropospheric station, Bahrain

coaxial cables had been introduced and the whole pendulum was swinging back again and everybody was saying, 'Well, forget about HF radio now, this is the way to go.' And the next thing was, they'd put satellites up and everybody was convinced that coaxial cables were finished. Then along comes fibre optic and we're laying cables under the sea again. It's so interesting the way the pendulum has swung backwards and forwards in my lifetime, several times backwards and forwards.

George Warwick, *with experience in many parts of the world before a lengthy stint in Hong Kong, considers the mind-set of the old cable-based Company that saw telephones as other peoples' concerns – with the difficulties that posed when Cable & Wireless itself in the course of the 1970s became ever more involved with local as well as international telephone systems paving the way for the present day.*

In the 1950s, even though the first telephone cable had already been laid, people thought that telegraph cables would still continue. I don't think many people actually foresaw the explosion in telecommunications that came, not even the forward-thinking people. I don't know why people didn't get to be forward-thinking. I suppose telegrams were being sent for so long, people thought they would continue for ever. That was the main part of our business, and really, until the 1960s there were a lot of people who didn't want to know about telephony. By then it was so clear it was the main thing ...

We had a long history of being a telegraph company and our experiments in local telephones had been very bad ones. We hadn't made any money on local telephones, largely because we wouldn't buy in the expertise we needed. There seemed to be a mental block. Cable & Wireless employed a number of people, and they were capable of doing anything that Cable & Wireless wanted done – so if you wanted a man to do this, you went through the list to see who was available.

John Fuge *describes the rigmarole involved in making an international telephone call in the pioneering days of the later 1930s.*

We had the second radio telephone service in the world, Bermuda to New York. We'd send a telegram to New York, this telegram would be delivered and the person would reply – it was a reply-paid telegram – Yes, they would be on the phone at 4 o'clock on Monday afternoon. Providing you got the yes, about an hour before this phone call, St George's [station] would have to start a diesel engine, a single-cylinder engine – you had to start it by getting a blowlamp out and pumping up and heating a bulb up, and when it was the right temperature you could spin the flywheel and the engine would start.

Once you'd got the engine started you could run up your transmitters and the receiving station would then call the distant end, and you'd make contact – and then the call would go through! That was done by somebody sitting on a device called a telephone terminal unit, a TTU, and they would control both the outgoing volume and the incoming volume to try and get the call through. They'd measure the call in total duration of time and in what they thought was good talk time, because that's what you were billed. So the ticket would say: duration of call 13 minutes, billed 3 minutes. Anyway, at the end of the call, if there wasn't another call, you'd switch it all off and wait for the next. So we've come a long way since then.

John Davenport *spent the middle part of the 1960s as one of the team implementing the new generation of submarine cables. They were planning developments on a scale hardly attempted since the pioneering days of cable-laying, and with capacities for message transmission that were unimaginable a decade, let alone almost a century before.*

I was posted into Head Office, nominally for three years; I went into the Engineering Department, and into a section which was concerned with laying coaxial cables. That involved a certain amount of retraining for me, and it involved a certain amount of travelling as we laid the SEACOM system around the Far East. It involved visits to places like Medang in New Guinea and Borneo and Guam in the Pacific, Hong Kong and Singapore. From my point of view that was interesting – and it was developing technology. There would be typically six weeks while we ... installed the equipment, tested it and connected it to the system, tested that and brought the system into service. And then we'd leave. We'd go back to London, co-ordinate all the results, produce the reports. And then start on the next one.

Ted Amor*'s fix-it attitude was put to effect in the Company's engineering department. Telex was the order of the day in the 1960s, and Cable & Wireless were keen to capitalise on its success and improve its usability.*

I'd been working on electronic telex, and at that time, the subscriber's telex set was about two foot square and table height, full of relays and things. We were getting a new generation of teleprinters, and at Smale House I was asked to produce an electronic telex control unit using modern techniques, integrated circuits, and it was virtually about the size of a small loaf of bread when it came out, it could be parked anywhere. So I went to Hong Kong to introduce it and explain it to the chaps.

John Worrall *was a junior member of the team that installed the Company's first satellite earth station, the shape of things to come, in 1965. The experience was, like so much else in the field of telecommunications engineering, a mixture of the exciting and the prosaic.*

On Ascension, we put up this Meccano-like earth station, which looked like nothing on earth: it was a converted radar mount with a purpose-built dish on the top, about 30 feet in diameter. Not like the big ones you see now, but it worked very well. I had the doubtful privilege of being the first

Cable laying for SEACOM

The relay station built on Suva for SEACOM

The SEACOM opening at Jesselton

person to actually speak on a Cable & Wireless link, because I was in charge of what they call the low frequency equipment, amongst which responsibility was testing the channels. So I had to talk to the other end.

The first words? Oh, I can't remember ... We were working to Andover in Maine, so it was probably, 'Hello, Andover' or something like that.

We had a monitor on, and to hear one's own voice come back from a satellite ... There's a considerable delay because of the path lag, and it's quite remarkable when you hear that. You do really believe that you're talking to a satellite. Up to this time it had all been, 'Well, is it really there?' You can't see it, you're just working as it were by faith.

John Fuge *returned to work in Bermuda, where he had been born. His father had been like him a roving member of the Company staff. The continuities over the years are sometimes quite as striking as the differences.*

The difference now from the past is, if you have a break in a piece of equipment potentially you've cut Bermuda off. We now have over 750 voice channels out of Bermuda. And that all can go wrong because of one piece of kit. It's all digital and if your timing source is out your service is going to go down, and the potential or the pressures you work under now are much, much greater.

Yet in talking to my father, the problems he faced were so similar. When we moved from analogue to digital service in Bermuda, this would be in the 1980s, we moved all our types of transmission across to digital, and we were the first international point, basically, outside the US to go fully digital. And so a lot of the experiments were done between the US and Bermuda with AT&T. So it was quite interesting: we were leading the world there on some things, but some of the problems we faced were due purely to do with timing. My dad would often say to me, 'How are things going?', and I'd say, 'Well, we've had this problem and that problem,' and he'd say, 'It's funny, we had the same problems with the old cable circuits.' And of course they did, because they were effectively digital. They solved them in a mechanical way:

they built some device that would store the messages or would actually build in a delay. We would be doing it electronically, but the principles being applied were exactly the same. Everyone would be running around saying, 'This new technology ...', and I'd come back and say, 'No, it's not so new. I can show you the 1930s Blue Book' – what they used to call them, engineering books, the Blue Books – which were apparently facing the same things but the solution was slightly more basic. It's funny how these things go.

INDEPENDENT NATIONS AND LOCALISATION

At the same time as the telegraph cable systems were entering their last phase of useful life, geopolitical change was also overtaking the Company. A system that had been tied into Britain's territorial and commercial empire was no longer appropriate as former colonies achieved independence, and as staff who came from the particular location felt that they could attain the same levels of skill and expertise as the expatriate staffs who ran, maintained and managed the far-flung outposts of the Cable & Wireless enterprise. From the very early 1960s, territory after territory achieved independence from Britain; in many cases, Cable & Wireless lost its complete control of a country's external communications, and a whole variety of economic and corporate partnerships emerged. In many instances, Cable & Wireless led rather than followed the trend, for political as well as economic reasons; experience in some places showed the capabilities of properly trained local people, and the assumed raison d'être *for a large British expatriate workforce began to evaporate. The need for communications at the time a nation became independent often produced far more work for the Company in the short term – to be followed by long-term restructuring in its previous monopoly position. The tide of change swept through Africa, the Caribbean, the Far East, and the Pacific. In South America, where Cable & Wireless had always faced competition, the demands of localisation were combined with the uncertainties of unstable political regimes so that eventually the Company has almost wholly withdrawn from that continent.*

Brian Pemberton *swiftly became one of the new 'breed' of Cable & Wireless employees, working in a variety of the non-traditional activities that were of increasingly critical importance in the 1960s and 1970s. He introduces the themes of localisation, independence and partnership that were the hallmark of those years.*

Cable & Wireless was a company which really was extraordinarily disparate, anything from a Pacific island through the Arabian Gulf to a Caribbean island. Because telecoms in those days were pretty expensive per unit the amount of service calls which went on (free for people in the business) was limited and kept solely to business, so there was no social chit-chat between stations. That was the fairly cautious – I was going to say parsimonious – very tightly controlled Cable & Wireless which stretched right round the world. But it had stupid things like a man in corporate headquarters who would buy the loo rolls for the mess in Bahrain and they would be shipped out.

It changed from the start of my time, and technology drove it – that, and small nations' natural desire to become independent.

In many cases where we'd been the sole provider our objective was always to remain the monopolist – it's a nice position if you can obtain it with the government's permission. But more often than not, particularly as they faced independence, they wanted a partnership with the Company; and more often than not, again, as a minority shareholder with the Company having the controlling shareholding.

Pat Cowan *in the early 1960s was stationed on the Indian Ocean island of Rodrigues, feeling far removed from the centres of action and of change.*

There was writing on the wall as to what was going to happen to the Company. At that time all the African countries were becoming independent, and the next phase of decolonisation was coming on ... A lot of the stuff that came out to us was what was happening in Singapore, what was happening in Hong Kong, what was happening in Africa. We wondered if there was going to be a Company anyway. OK, we knew that radio was taking off but it was only just the beginning of thoughts of satellite and telephone cables ... There were no real plans for Rodrigues other than as a cable station – if you were looking at revenue there wasn't a lot that was going to be produced in an island like Rodrigues.

George Warwick *was in West Africa meanwhile for independence in the former Gold Coast in 1961.*

We had the freedom celebrations: Gold Coast became Ghana. It was a sad thing really because there were two Europeans at this particular station, four African watchkeepers and, say, fifteen to twenty labouring staff. Some of the African staff truly believed when they got freedom, they would get more money and things would be so much better and they really were looking forward to it. But nothing changed.

Maurice Bane *was one of the people who implemented a different form of change shortly thereafter in the new Ghana, when the new nation took over responsibility for its own telecommunications. He had been stationed there more than ten years previously, and was to find a wholly different situation.*

I was told, 'We've got a very difficult thing to do, and that is we want you to go to Ghana – because it's all been finalised and Ghana's taking over the telecommunications – and close down the shop and hand over to them.' Even before I'd got there all the contracts had been signed, so the four houses we had there, and all the contents of the messes – this lovely old silver which went back to the African Direct Telegraph days, 60 or 70 years old, everything that was on the inventories – had to be handed over. They'd paid for it in the total package.

The Company offices in Kingston decked out to celebrate
Jamaica's independence in 1962

Going back to Ghana was a very different kettle of fish because by that time it was independent and Nkrumah was riding high, and in that first period of time he was running it pretty well. We had about eight or nine expatriates there, and by the time I got there they were beginning to integrate. Our chaps had to train the Ghanaians on the equipment. By that time radio had developed quite considerably, it was semi-automatic instead of people sitting on terminals, and it was all very much better. We had TORS [Teleprinter On Radio] installed. We had a new complex system working to Nigeria on the cable. So it had all been upgraded since I was last there ...

I got there and found, for example, that the houses were in a bad state of repair. We were fortunate inasmuch as that by that time in West Africa, Ghana had gone, and Sierra Leone and Lagos were in the process of going, so the Managing Director by this time used to have to come to West Africa every three months and do a tour along the coast, just to show a face, and talk to the West African authorities there, and find if there was any chance of making any other deals. This was Henry Eggers, an ex-Treasury man, very charming, quirky; some people didn't get along with him too well, but fortunately I seemed to get along with him quite well ... By this time the Russians had moved in and all the embassies had been set up, the Czechoslovak Embassy, Russian Embassy, Chinese Embassy were all there, and the American Embassy of course. West Africa was beginning to turn Communist, quite worrying in many ways, and Nkrumah was flirting with Russia. So much so that we found things were very restricted. The food supplies we used to get weren't coming from UK. They didn't have the foreign currency, you couldn't send any foreign currency out of the country, and we had a large reserve of cash in the Bank of West Africa, which, of course, the Company couldn't remit, and the currency had been changed. I think individuals could send 15 per cent of their salary back or something. My wife at least got to know people there who had access to Ghana Airways' food supplies. It was also rather difficult because some of the expats we had there, five or six bachelors, youngish chaps, found it a bit hard getting along with the West Africans, one or two of whom were a bit insulting. We were now in a foreign country and the Ghanaians resented any show of colonialism, so you trod a very careful path ...

We had to be careful because there were always people on the watch, and of course, the old, old story: Nkrumah was King. You'd be driving along the road, and suddenly motorcycles would come roaring down the road, saying 'Ebah, ebah', which means, 'He comes, he comes'. You had to pull your car to the side of the road, and if there wasn't room enough, you had to put your car in the ditch to clear the way for him, because all the guards were frightened of assassination. He was always tremendously well-protected, and he wore a bullet-proof vest all the time. Meanwhile the country was deteriorating: the cocoa crop was being ruined, because all the farmers said, 'We don't have to bother now, it's our land, our crops.' All the up-country farms were getting cocoa blight and the quality of the cocoa was going down, and instead of being bought up by Cadbury's and Fry's, it was being put on the Russian ships as barter for the Russians ... All the big stores were taken over and nationalised. They were mainly run by the Lebanese, who virtually ran the west coast. You would go into the stores, and they would be stacked full of tins; you'd pick one up, and it was all in Russian or Czech. There was no picture on it to tell you what it was, so you didn't know whether it was pilchards, or bacon, or sausages, or whatever. So food was a problem. We used to buy these tins, take them home and open them, and we'd try and find out what they were ...

I had to tread a delicate course with the Director of Telecommunications and a couple of other chaps. Of course, there was still the basic staff there that had been before, so I knew them quite well, but the other people coming in from the P & T were not so easy to deal with. There were a number of upsets with some of our youngsters, and clashes with the local staff ... But it went fairly smoothly, and we moved along towards a handover situation. I was there about eighteen months, but felt growing apprehension that it might all go wrong ...

Herbie Blundell *spent a considerable part of his Company career training local people in a succession of countries to maintain and take over the running of their own telecommunications. The process began in Nigeria in 1963, among the first of the new partnerships to be established, that within three years was to be wholly owned by the Nigerian government. In these cases, existing Cable & Wireless staff were retained and to have no diminution in their pay and privileges, but their presence would naturally wither speedily.*

Nigeria had just become independent, and while I was there Cable & Wireless ceased to exist and NET, the Nigerian External Telecoms, came into force. It was a difficult time: some of the lads didn't like it at all, there was no doubt about that. I have a letter still from the then Managing Director, Wilf Davies, saying this is what is going to happen and this is how it is going to be, and it may be that some of you don't like what is taking place but ... it was a joint venture. I then had to run two training schools, one in the morning and one in the afternoon. We had a big expansion programme. I had also to select people to go off for training in the UK. Most of the staff were in Lagos, there were a handful at Kano, in northern Nigeria. I liked the Nigerians, in fact I enjoyed teaching them, there was a thirst and quest for knowledge.

In 1962 I had been to Barbados, and I ran the training school there. For the first time ever I ran classes for the promotion to supervisor and management grades as well. It was the first time the older West Indian guys had had what we call serious training. In fact, some of those chaps I trained there went on to become System Managers and Human Resources Managers in the Caribbean later. The Company were very clever in the way they did things then: you were training future Cabinet Ministers, that's what it came to. Archie Willett was the Managing Director at the time: I think the way he set things up in the Caribbean and the way he looked at the future, we wouldn't have as many friends in the Caribbean now if we hadn't done what we were doing then, thirty-five years ago. It was a far-sighted exercise.

My wife and I enjoyed Barbados, a nice island, very nice people, big staff and a big Company. I ended up playing rugby for Barbados against Harlequins when they visited; and against the USS *Boxer* when they visited us which was a very interesting afternoon, because they played American football while we played rugby! ...

I spent the twelve years from 1965 in Bermuda. People pull my leg about that. When I went every single job was held by an Englishman, except for the two people on the counter and the phone room staff who were Bermudians, while the rest were part-timers, all of Portuguese extraction. But all the engineering staff were White Anglo-Saxon Protestants, and they were costing an arm and a leg as were the operators. My job was to find and train Bermudians and phase them in, and I was given a five-year programme. That placed me in a difficult position with a lot of my colleagues because they said, 'Look, you're doing us out of a job' ... And within five years we had Bermudian technicians on the rounds, the whole of the instrument room had been Bermudianised, with a mixture of white Portuguese and black Bermudians. I deliberately set out to do that. And the only [F1] left were the two supervisors, and the next phase was they were to go.

Sonny Gilkes *was among the very first Barbados-born employees to acquire a full engineering training with Cable & Wireless, in due course becoming the island company's Chief Engineer and then a senior manager with the successor joint venture company BET. A number of the men he worked alongside left Cable & Wireless to enter Barbadian politics.*

I went to Washington DC once to visit my sister. She was ill. [My brother-in-law] met me at the airport, and said, 'I'm very sorry, can I take you straight to my ... meeting.' The meeting was in the city, and the Barbados Minister of Health was there, an ex-Cable & Wireless man. He came over, he said: 'Yes! Sonny! How are you?' 'Well, I'm fine.' 'Come into the meeting. Come and sit with the Barbados representatives.' I said I didn't have a tie on. I'd just put on a blazer, I was casual. He said, 'No, you come in.' So I went in, and joined the Barbados delegation. Now he is an ex-Cable & Wireless

New equipment comes to the old town in Muscat

man. And every time we met, although he was a minister of government, we were like *that.* In fact a number of ex-Cable & Wireless people were ministers of government. It's rather fantastic. And we still have that close relationship whenever we see each other.

John Worrall *worked in a number of situations in which Cable & Wireless entered into a partnership, often on a 51:49 split in the joint interest, with the local government.*

We'd all been training local staff as a matter of course. Wherever we were in the late 1960s and early 1970s, we were almost always on the retreat. For instance, the group of us who were installing the earth station in Trinidad were the last employees. And we weren't actually employed by Cable & Wireless there, we were employed by TEXTEL, the Trinidad and Tobago External Telecoms. We were seconded to them. While we were installing, and commissioning, and operating that earth station, we were training their staff to take our jobs. When we moved out, we weren't replaced, so we were the last of a breed in that sense.

Gustavo Coll *has lived through tremendous change in South America. In his native Montevideo, the capital of Uruguay, he joined Cable & Wireless, the Western Telegraph Company, and received an engineering training. Gradually the British presence in this part of the 'informal empire' diminished, as did the traffic on the old telegraph cables. New enterprises were to be established here, as elsewhere in South America, to compensate for dwindling traffic and the competitive environment. The ending of franchises, political upheaval and corporate decisions to concentrate activity elsewhere led to Cable & Wireless's virtual disappearance from South America.*

When I joined the Company, I remember listening to older people: at the beginning, even the operators were British people. But when I joined the Company only the engineers, the commercial gentleman, plus the manager, were all British. Ten of them, roughly. I'll use this expression as a term of endearment. They were *gringos*. Some of them were very much respected, of course. The manager was always an aloof figure, but I had no problem with that ... In the 1950s, the British community here was fairly large. In those days we had a lot of insurance companies, the British shipping companies. The gas company was British. We still had a lot of English people who were ex-railways, because the railways had been nationalised in 1950 and some of them decided to stay in Uruguay. And so it was fairly large: the British colony I should call it ...

Not having submarine cables and a limited amount of traffic to Montevideo, something had to be done. There was no need for so many expatriate staff. And the commercial department, which had traditionally been run by an expatriate, was being run by a local too. I was made engineer, and eventually I was made manager of the company. The last expatriate left in 1972 when I took over from him. But let's face it, Montevideo was a minuscule branch in those days. It was the last Western Telegraph branch. We were a bit of a bother in Head Office: a branch with thirty people, forty people, not much contribution or even none at all. So it was a bother to them ...

Cable & Wireless came to an end in Uruguay on 31 December 1980. I closed it down. I had had to fire a lot of people, because we no longer had the cables to Brazil or to Argentina and we only had one circuit to London, so I had to take some harsh measures. But we were finally closed down because of the government. It happened in Peru and Brazil, in Chile, in Argentina. We had it all over South America: we had military governments and they would say, 'We don't want our communications to be run by a foreign company.' Even today, unless you are a big power your communications are run by somebody else unless you have the capability of sending a satellite or laying your own cable. Uruguay can't do that ...

It was decided that after so many years in Uruguay it would be a pity, a

The opening of the new St Vincent exchange in 1969

shame, to lose our presence here and with the invaluable help of Ron Werngren we started what is this company today, still called Westec, Western Technical Services. Even though I was a manager of a respected English telegraph company, I started peddling magnetic tapes door to door, because I saw this as the only way I could survive. And eventually things took off. So when we closed down Western Telegraph, Westec had already been formed. We were only two people, we started growing and everything went well up to the Falklands affair. At that time the Company decided that they were not all that keen on their involvement with small business systems or centres in South America. So they closed down Westec in Buenos Aires and they closed down Westec here. Actually, closing down is not the right word. They sold it. They sold Westec in Argentina to two Argentine gentlemen, and they sold Westec here to me.

Pat Cowan *was working in Lima, Peru in the late 1960s, one of the fast-dwindling band of British expatriates working in the South American operations, and able to see the writing on the wall.*

In Lima, there again we were being threatened by nationalisation. It was at the end of my time there that the government put in their first earth station, and then all the routing was taken away from our regular stations and routed through the government earth station. Gradually Cable West Coast kind of died, as did many of our other South American operations at that time, the end of the 1960s. Then we started seeing our leading position in South America generally, in Brazil, Argentina, Peru and to a lesser extent Bolivia, being taken away. Things started to go, and certainly the governments wanted to take over our telecommunications interests there. That was after it had all happened in Africa, and that was quite interesting to observe.

Patricia Bosdet *was in tax and investment appraisal during the early 1970s, and therefore at the sharp end of the new corporate ventures the Board was initiating.*

Henry Eggers was quite keen to set up joint companies. He felt that was the way forward, to go into partnership with the governments. It was a central strategy. He was going round the world talking to governments, and suggesting they set up joint ventures.

We were therefore progressing towards a joint company with the Fiji government. I went out there with Wilfred Davies (who was a Director, and the next Head of Personnel in the Staff Department). When we got there I think we had the feeling that perhaps the Fiji government weren't terribly keen to take over a stake in the Company after all. They felt there must be something wrong with it and we were trying to lumber them with part of the Company – whereas we went out there on the understanding that they were terribly keen and wanted to participate ...

We went on from there to the Solomon Islands where Cable & Wireless had not previously been. We were asked to go into the Solomon Islands, and we set up a company there.

I went on the Board of FINTEL when it was set up, which is the external telecommunications company ... It was interesting to be involved in the negotiations for the joint company in Fiji, and then to go on and see it into company status. It seemed to be an unfortunate time to be selling because we'd just had a lot of capital expenditure. We put in this huge Standard A station, which had been heavy capital expenditure, and we were just gradually seeing the profits. So we were selling out almost on the basis of an inflated asset value at the time. There was all this heavy expenditure, and then the profits were coming in later – so perhaps not the time you'd have chosen from a business point of view.

I think it was driven by the feeling at that time that many governments didn't want the colonial power running their communications, so it was felt it was sensible to withdraw. For some of the places we pulled out of, Cable & Wireless went gradually to a minority stake – and since then have come back in and taken a majority stake.

Sidney Sherwood, *who had been based in Fiji previously when he was an engineer on cable ships, returned there as General Manager in the late 1970s with Joan, his wife.*

Yes, some of the local staff I knew, not terribly well, but odd ones were still there. There were no expats left that I had known. In fact there were only four expats at that time: myself, an accountant, a chief engineer and a traffic chap. All the rest were local, because gradually all the jobs were being localised all the time. I found it a marvellous job: preparing Board papers, you had to do them yourself, then submitting them to the Board of Directors who sat in on them, and you could plan for the whole Company. And also times had moved on from the old days, I think way back, probably the local and expat staff didn't mix that well, but when I was there, they had this local sports club and there were lots of activities going on all the time, parties, with the local staff, so that helped; that was excellent and helped a lot.

Joan Sherwood: And of course, when we were first there it was still the old Governor in his frilled hat. We were actually in Fiji when it was handed over – we have it on film. It was very much the old colonial lifestyle then, but that all changed.

Brian Pemberton *was involved in many of the new types of activity that Cable & Wireless pursued from the mid-1960s – special contracts, secondment to the agencies of newly independent former colonies, private business services – beginning in Bahrain. Ultimately, he was given overall charge of Hong Kong that had become the financial jewel in the Company's crown.*

We were basically given a bit of desert by the ruler of Bahrain and went out there, built an HF radio station first, then subsequently a tropospheric scatter system which worked down to Doha.

Now, I had an atlas. But when I got to grips with it, Bahrain wasn't quite the Caribbean island I'd been led to expect. I had a great time there, I made friendships there and, because of the new technology, I had interesting jobs that I was asked to do for the ruling family. Of course, there, if the ruler wanted something, then the ruler got it. When they were hunting in the desert, they could now talk to each other with the old, very early walkie-talkie mobile phones – which weren't these slim handsome things, they were rather large, back-pack type of things.

Then to Malawi, to what had become East African Telecoms. I was on secondment there. The East African Federation was starting to work and Robin Forest, who was the boss man, had got involved in some discussions whereby there was a possibility the Company could get into Malawi. With Hastings Banda taking power, he had not wanted to cut all Malawi's links with Rhodesia, because it wasn't practical. But where he could – rather than being 'long lined' off a telephone exchange in Salisbury which is effectively what Malawi was – he wanted someone to help him out to make him more independent in his telecoms. Cable & Wireless sent me down there to help them keep going what they'd got, and then to act as Project Manager, if I could get Malawi to agree the funding for new facilities.

It was a great time for me because I was really my own boss ... I was given by the powers-that-be a Government purchase order book, an E107, which I shall never forget. Once you were an authorised signatory on an E107, you could literally go into the Government stores and ... You could have ordered an aircraft, I guess, if you felt so inclined, because you were an authorised signatory. I was still fairly young then, but it was marvellous because I was able, with the guys who were there, to design a new transmitting station and a new receiving station. We had the land and everything, and we used the E107s to call up the Marconi transmitters and receivers and so forth, and together with some younger guys from Cable & Wireless and some very good Malawian people we put them in. We gave Banda what he wanted, which was to communicate with the rest of the world via Nairobi, rather than being dependent on Salisbury. I think there was probably in his mind a genuine fear that Smith might pull the plug ... and in any case in Commonwealth forums he wouldn't have wanted to look as if he was overly dependent on that regime.

I had a period then of working in Head Office, corporate HQ, and that lasted five or six years. At the time we had just taken on board John Bird, at board level, whose responsibility was to create a replacement business for the – as perceived at that time – shrinking franchise business. We'd lost African concessions, we'd gone into partnership with some of the Caribbean ones. The powers-that-be at that time thought, 'If we lose them all, what the hell are we going to do?' John Bird came in from outside the telecoms industry: he wasn't a telecoms service person, but he was a great character and leader. He chose me as one of his group officials to run private systems business. So, for instance, I'd say, 'Look, there are oil companies around the world, or other entities, who see telecoms as absolutely vital for them but don't want to have a huge telecoms headquarters being an overhead on them.' I'd got particularly good relations with Shell at that time, and with their man who was responsible for telecoms systems, and we put some systems in for them under the private systems business. These were turnkey projects with a maintenance ongoing, of so many men at so much a year, according to what the customer wanted.

That became a business which I ran profitably, although in relationship to the mainline business it wouldn't have grown fast enough to replace the loss of, say, Hong Kong or the Caribbean. But it was growing quite nicely. I learnt all the problems that occur with people and projects going wrong, and all the best-laid plans getting thrown up in the air by a [nation's] ruler, or something ... [Bird] was keen amongst the Directors to prove that these lines of business, with government contracts and private systems business, could in due course replace the losses we were having on the franchises.

It was an entirely prudent line to take ... You realised there was no God-given right that all the franchises would be renewed. [It was a] failed attempt, if you like, over ten or fifteen years, to bring up the non-concessional business so that as one went down, the other came up and would continue to grow ... It was quite a change in Cable & Wireless. One of the dangers of Cable & Wireless was that it was a fairly insulated specialised business which

you were good at and ran well, but there was no guarantee that it was going to happen for ever more. People used to blanch if you said at the board meetings, 'Well, what happens if you lose Hong Kong?' 'We won't lose Hong Kong, it's too valuable to us.' 'We have to have some streams of revenue that are new and growing and have potential in the long term to become another Hong Kong.'

FRANCHISES AND NEW BUSINESS

If the soul of Cable & Wireless was still in its traditional telecommunications activity and places where it had long had a presence, its lifeblood became a whole range of additional activities. Many were associated with telecommunications in both old and new forms, but the list and variety of new enterprises increased substantially. The search for new business as the old core activities were restricted drove the Company on, particularly in the difficult years it experienced in the 1970s. The old spirit of adventure was never very far away. In some instances, particularly in the Middle East, old relationships were built upon; new business partnerships were formed; and sometimes old alliances were rediscovered.

Patricia Bosdet *had worked for some length of time in the Fixed Assets Department of Head Office, and was on the receiving end of many of the changes being wrought in the 1970s.*

You had to write up every time you bought a [fixed] asset and state what it was and where it was. You waited until it depreciated, and that also had to be written onto the cards. Because you were writing it up, you became very familiar with where all the assets were. They were in all these strange

The Kuwait earth station opening ceremony

Servicing the Apollo missions:

Left: Aerial under construction, Ascension Island.

Below: Staff at Bermuda tracking station

Bottom: The crew of Apollo 8 prepare for the start of their mission

places, and we had some fascinating telegraph cables, like Banana Two Piece, and Banjawoengie to wherever. Fascinating names that you got to know. In those days the Company operated in a lot of areas which it left – and many years later, wanted to go back into. The management at that time would say, 'Oh, we've got an opportunity to go into Singapore, or Egypt,' or perhaps even Dublin, and I would say, 'Well, we were in there twenty-five years ago, and we left.' People did not realise that the Company had had such a wide spread of overseas operations.

John Slaughter *began his working life with Marconi, and was an early specialist in satellite communications. He subsequently moved across to Cable & Wireless, and found himself with some remarkable experiences in the field. Later in his career he became intimately involved in finding new areas of business and countries to deal with, taking his exploring and technical zeal into commercial operations.*

I had been designing satellite earth stations, and had been working with Cable & Wireless engineers, and I made the change in 1970. I started in fact not in the satellite field at all, but microwave, and I took over as the section leader for microwave projects in the Western hemisphere to start with, the Caribbean and parts of Africa, that went across into Middle East as well.

It was real ground-breaking stuff. Everyone thought we were mad. Nobody thought we'd ever do it.

I'd been struggling looking to see how we could do it: the longest hop between microwave relay stations that we had on paper was about 150 miles, and we couldn't do it. Seventy miles was held to be reasonable ... 150 miles wasn't possible. My colleague Alan Knight and I were looking at a map of the region, one we hadn't looked at before, just of the Leeward Islands. I said, if we could only get a microwave tower on St Martin that was 3,000 feet high ... And we looked, and there just south of St Martin was a little dot – it was an island called Saba, and it had a population of a thousand people, it was five miles across, and 3,000 feet high ...

That journey across to Saba itself was another thing. There were three people on the boat with me. One of them was Bob Yamarach, the mechanic, who looked after all the vehicles in Tortola for the telephone system. He came along in case the engines broke down. There was Captain Pickering, an old schooner captain who'd been taken on to be captain of this boat. He was drunk the whole journey because he'd found the beer at 5 o'clock in the morning before we got on board. And the chap who saved our lives really, was Josh. Josh was also from schooners, a younger bloke, who had a bad leg and couldn't stand up for very long. Well, Bob Yamarach had violent seasickness, Captain Pickering was drunk, and Josh couldn't stand up for very long, so I had to drive it all the way to Saba. And what I knew about boats could be written on the back of an envelope ...

When we got there, there was this pebbly beach and the ground dropped away quite quickly from that. Bob Yamarach and I, the two who had nothing to do with boats at all, got in the dinghy. We both had our life jackets on, Bob was rowing in for the shore, among great big waves. The other chap who was meeting us there, so we could start doing some surveys, had flown in on a little aeroplane. He'd got the Administrator of the island, the Governor, in tow, and they came down to meet us because somebody had sighted us. Everybody knows what's going on all the time on Saba, mostly from this primitive telephone system they had, all passing messages on it and no-one was charged for it. I'd seen these two little figures there on the beach; we were rowing away, I was at the front of the boat, and we realised we were going to have to do something fairly dramatic when we got to the beach. Otherwise we were going to be thrown on the beach and then swept off again. So we landed on the shingle, I jumped out and grabbed the boat so Bob didn't get away in it. The next thing I knew, I was looking at the side of the boat, and he was suspended in the water. I was still standing on the shingle so I pulled it further in, completely soaked. To be greeted by the Administrator.

Saba was a nightmare of a site. Just over 3,000 feet, and the nearest place you could get a vehicle to (and there weren't many vehicles on the island anyway) was at 1,400 feet. Everything had to be carried or helicopter-lifted, and helicopter trips would be quite hairy as well. What we had to do was to put two power cables up from this 1,400-feet level. We had to buy a field at that level to build a small power station on to power this thing at the top, which had to have enough power to run a TV transmitter, because the Dutch, who owned the island, wouldn't let us build a site up there unless we put in enough power to run a TV transmitter. All very political, in a nice friendly sort of way.

I was telling 'Tug' Wilson back at Head Office that it was going to be very difficult to get things up there: 'I think we need a helicopter.' He said, 'Why do you need a helicopter, you could hire the donkeys?' I had put in one of the reports, which he'd read – and I'd forgotten – that there were two donkeys on the island, used to bring bananas down from the top of the mountain. We tried to use one of the donkeys to take the survey gear up. But halfway up a 200-feet sheer face, with rock steps cut into it – it was just like a rock step ladder 200 feet long, the steps in some cases about 2 feet wide – the donkey stopped. He wouldn't go, and he had bits of tower and test equipment and things on his back. He just wouldn't go any more. So we had to unload the donkey. [The men] unloaded the donkey and carried all the rest of the equipment up the steps, and then they came back and picked up the donkey and carried him up.

We got up top. Loaded it all up and got up to the top. I rode the donkey at the top, just to show him who was boss.

On Grenada, a local guide accompanied the intrepid engineer to the top of one of that island's mountains.

I found a site, we chopped a few trees down and took some measurements. But on the way up I really wondered if I was going to get down again. In tropical rain forests, it's seriously slippery: a lot of green vegetation, and lianas hanging down, really dense cover at the bottom, then you have these great trees that go up for miles, and it's another world up there. We were climbing up one of these cliffs; in one or two places we had to climb up trees, they would bend in, and we could get onto the cliff again. And I *knew* we weren't going to get a road up here. (We did find someone to put a road up in the end.) On the last bit of that particular trip I'd done this trick of going up the tree and bending it in to another bit so I could start climbing, but there was an overhang at the

Aerial view of Saba, the critical stepping stone in the Caribbean microwave link

top of the cliff – and this overhang was the roots of the tree that had grown out around the overhang. That was I think my worst experience on a mountain. I was hanging upside down, and this guide – an old man, to me then he was extremely old – just shinned up over it. I really thought I'd had it. I thought, 'I can't tell him I can't get up there.' I did it in the end. I remember thinking, 'I didn't know about this as part of radio engineering.'

We didn't make a big fuss about the fact that this was ground-breaking, we didn't go around saying this is a wonderful new achievement because that would have scared [the Company] to death. The competing cable alternative would have gone to fewer places and cost five or six times as much.

That was a fantastic project, and about three years later – I can't remember what I was doing, but I was flying from Miami – we went over some islands, and I was looking at a map and thinking they were the American Virgin Islands. And thinking, 'It's amazing what these Americans can do. When there's enough money and enough gumption, the things you can do.' I was looking down at what seemed like an incredible technical complex, right on top of a mountain – and then I realised I was flying over Saba. I'd never seen it from the air before.

Howard Kleyn *worked for a considerable time in Hong Kong. Having installed the first automatic exchange, he followed the wave of diversification that was sweeping through Cable & Wireless in the 1970s.*

I joined an organisation which was CWS, Cable & Wireless Systems. It was effectively a subsidiary of the main branch, dedicated to offering specialised telecoms services to particular sections of the market. We put in an automated totalisator at the race course. When the people are making their bets and so on and you're flashing the signals out to these infield indicators to show the racing public what the odds are and how they are changing, it's all communications. The next task was to put in one of these toll collection systems for the cross-harbour tunnel. Again, it's communications: you collect the money from the motorist and the data has to be sent up to some processor which works out what the totals are, and whether the chap in the booth is sticking to any of the money and so on. We got many contracts of that kind, some of which were the precursors to others further afield.

Colin Sharp *provides one example of the 'can do' nature of the work that the Company was undertaking increasingly from the later 1960s. No amount of self-sufficient cable station training had prepared its engineers for some ventures.*

The Company had a terrible job out in Seychelles. They had to change the island.

They'd worked out in the Foreign Office that the island should be independent – but it couldn't be independent unless it had something to self-support it. So we were all assigned. I went with my wife to Bombay in December 1968 and together with the other consignees – who consisted of a large group of dynamite specialists, from Costains – we all went on one boat the day before Christmas to Seychelles. We passed Christmas at sea. We arrived in Seychelles: then the island used to get something like, shall we say, a dozen people a year ...

We had to change the island totally: we had to install new telephone exchanges, put in a receiving station for HF, a transmitting station for HF, a basis for a satellite station and connect both receiving and transmitting stations by HF. We had to have a link down to the new airport.

And of course Seychelles never was the same again.

We took out with us the largest dredger in the world at that time. They'd had to lay down the airport – but to make the airport you first of all had to remove a mountain. That's where the dynamiters came in, and every day at midday *bing* went one extra piece of mountain. The locals for years used to reclaim tiny pieces of ground, about the size of my sitting room. They used patiently to lay rocks around it, and then fill it in with a little bit of earth. That's how they thought we were going to do the airport. [Until] nine months to a year after our getting there, the locals did not really think that the airport would really work or was going to be.

It was a lot of work. We had no extra people at all. I was the chief engineer. My manager used to come out about 10 in the morning, then he would disappear about 4 in the afternoon. He managed to sign the accounts and papers and that was about the end of it. So everything in the island, because it was an engineering project, was more or less mine. Including the building of these two big HF receiving and transmitting sites. We had to put telephone exchanges in Frayling Island, which is just off the coast of Seychelles, so we had to undertake such things as building rafts – forty-gallon oil drums, putting wood on top, then putting the bulldozer on it and towing it across. Very primitive, but it all got done.

There was myself, the Clerk of Works, and we had one installation man who came in, but that was all. During that time we built the two stations, we'd surveyed and put in the VHF links, we'd put in the new telephone exchanges, and we'd arranged with a local builder to put in something like twenty residences for the new staff. We left there in 1972, and after we were relieved I think something like twenty people came to take over from us.

John Slaughter *became subsequently one of the new breed of people who went out to sell what the Company could or might offer, wherever and whenever opportunity arose.*

The Standard B earth stations were giving us an entrée into a lot of countries. That meant that with the countries I first went to, first of all there was no Cable & Wireless operation, in the main (one or two did have them), and also they were countries which were between somewhat and extremely under-developed. So in Central America, I spent quite a bit of time in El Salvador – the civil war was starting there – and Guatemala. We actually set up the earth stations and ran them for a while.

At that time we weren't really sure what we were trying to do. We were looking at an ultimate objective in trying to get an international franchise to operate in telecoms, preferably a monopoly. There was a general feeling we shouldn't get involved in telephone systems themselves and that proved to be wrong; but to a number of countries, places like the Pacific islands where I spent quite a bit of time, we were their main operator then. Still are. Those places had such bad communications that you could make a very good case for a big foreign company coming in and running the international, and generating more revenue for the telephone company. Generally helping them to develop, but not investing in it. I think that's now impossible, but at that time it was possible ...

My job was guarding the doors at that stage. It was quite easy to go in to talk to people to start with. You could always break the ice by just telling them about Cable & Wireless. They were used to having salesmen come in telling them about equipment. What we were trying to do was a bit different, and we could get people's imagination with it. The treatment I found was to find one or two champions (it didn't really matter what level they were), on occasions it was the International Telecommunications Union adviser, and then use that as a window into the Company. Occasionally it might be the Permanent Secretary or whoever it was that looked after telecoms, and at other times it might be the chap who was looking after the radio systems.

You sense when you're talking to people if you're being accepted, and there's a sort of willingness to help. Every place was different.

John Slaughter (right) meets and greets

I was working in Africa for a time: the main work was in Botswana where we eventually ran Teletswana. Set it up and ran it for fourteen or fifteen years. They were just starting the development of the country. A very conservative government with, at that time, 1.5 million people, in a place the size of Western Europe. A tremendous natural wealth in diamonds, and the main beef producer in that part of the world. They had everything going for them, and they were really quite remarkable people. We spent quite a time getting into that: they were very careful, went one step at a time. That was a case of wandering into the Ministry of Telecommunications the first day I was there, knocking on a couple of doors and asking to see the Permanent Secretary. Meeting someone who was the Deputy and just starting to chat to him.

Wally Hardiman *was the first Chief Executive of one of the largest-ever of Cable & Wireless's contract projects, SANGCOM, providing a communications system for the Saudi Arabian National Guard. This was to prove in many ways the Company's salvation given the scale of the job, the numbers it employed and the revenue it generated.*

There was no good in having paper engineers in Saudi Arabia, I had to have roustabouts when we first went out there, which was 1974. Eventually I got a team of seven to go out. I had Stan Green as Project Engineer, an architect, a traffic man, an HF radio engineer and a couple of microwave engineers, a training man and myself ... Though we were a very unorthodox crew, it worked. We spent – I spent – seven years in and out of Saudi. I did a total of about 50 trips in and out of Saudi, and we built up a project from nothing. The first phase alone was £360 million.

We trained an awful lot of staff for Saudi Arabia: microwave engineers, tropospheric scatter engineers. We gave them tremendous experience. We had a staff of over a hundred UK staff out there, plus Pakistani, local and Sudanese people, so we had a total of 500. Plus a £90 million contract for Taylor Woodrow building works, which we supervised throughout. It was a hard life to start with because in 1974, 1975, Saudi was only just becoming alive. There was only one hotel in Riyadh. It was the only time in my life I've ever slept with other men in the same double bed, because we could only get one hotel room. And I was a first grade F1 officer – which in Hong Kong was something pretty good, you know. You lived in the Mandarin Hotel and places like that in Hong Kong – and I was in Saudi Arabia, sharing a double bed, in a grotty hotel.

And there was intrigue, because we had to go into the realms of lawyers in Saudi Arabia together with the British Ministry of Defence and many interesting National Guard personnel, notably General Abdul Aziz al Ayar.

It was great because it was completely different – but you had to have staff who weren't used to, say, going in from Hong Kong in a motor car every day, getting to the office, sitting in an air-conditioned office. Eventually it all came to be like that in Saudi, but it was just about as I was retiring that we got those conditions.

Ron Werngren *was a member of the second wave of experienced Cable & Wireless personnel who joined the SANGCOM project.*

A Director said, 'We want you in Saudi in a year's time.' I thought, 'Oh, yes. This isn't Cable & Wireless as I know Cable & Wireless,' because they couldn't tell you what you were going to do in two weeks' time, let alone in a year's time. Almost to the day I was stepping off the plane in Riyadh a year later.

I had the title of Manager, SANGCOM. For the Saudi Arabian National Guard. And I've never seen a man so relieved as the man I relieved. It was a complicated situation. Cable & Wireless had been working for years to try and get a contract to give the National Guard in Saudi Arabia decent communications. Literally years and years and years. They finally got it, but the only way they could do it was Government to Government, so we were in fact working to the Ministry of Defence, and the MoD was working with

Saudi ... We presented a more or less united front to the Saudis, but we had to do everything.

It was an HF system, not even VHF. HF system, and there were nodes throughout Saudi Arabia. Ar Ar in the North, Dhahran in the East, Riyadh, Nejran down south, Taif, Jeddah. In each place we built from scratch the buildings, the water supply, sewerage, you name it, and ultimately communications. It was a very, very big and complex enterprise. Fraught with difficulty ... Living materially was good. You could get anything you wanted there except alcohol and pork, and if you knew an American company you could get those as well. But they had a technique: you weren't allowed to do anything actually, but they'd turn a blind eye to things. And if they wanted you, they had you.

It didn't bother me because my wife came out as soon as possible, which was a few months after I got there. Initially we lived in the Manager's house: it was a bit of a slum because it had eight bedrooms but only seven bathrooms, you know. But it was spooky, it was so big it was spooky. Head Office would come out and make free and expect to be looked after, and we got fed up, so I decided we would move next door but one, where there was a set of six flats, two-bedroom flats, with nice kitchens, living area, a pool. I think everybody thought we were crazy, but of an evening we'd gather by the pool and have a communal barbecue.

It was a very pleasant, sociable life. Except that women couldn't drive, and if they went out they had to be reasonably covered up. There was a mini-bus that went out every day to go round the place for women to go shopping or whatever. The supermarkets were like ones I've never seen before or ever since. There were no cinemas, theatres, no communal entertainment at all. It just wasn't allowed. There were what was known as religious police, and if you were caught out with a woman who wasn't your wife, you were both in very severe trouble. The fact that there was no alcohol meant everybody was brewing their own beer like mad. In the supermarkets they sold European juices; the bottles were the flip top type you can seal down again. And it'd been known for the checkout man to say, 'Haven't you forgotten the yeast, sir?' Because it was made to measure for brewing. It got to ridiculous proportions ...

Herbie Blundell *joined the SANGCOM team later still, in 1981. His role was to keep the project on schedule. The style of expatriate life that characterised most of Cable & Wireless's activities there was, as for the oil companies and other British overseas enterprises, wholly different from the traditional pattern.*

I must admit that was probably the most educational time of my life. We had something like three thousand people who went through the Saudi project in the four years I was there. I met an enormous number of people. One of my first jobs – we were behind schedule, and about to start getting into penalty clauses – was to increase the working week from 48 to 60 hours. I toured all the sites. They were straight out of the Arabian Nights really. I had to go round the Riyadh sites, then to Damman, Jeddah, Taif, Hofuf, Nejran, and Ar Ar, talk to everybody, and say, 'This is where we are, this is what we're going to do, get back on schedule, and there's a bonus in it for you.' Only one guy said he didn't want to do it, so we put him on a plane and sent him home. His wife gave me hell ...

Basically, the chaps living there got up in the morning, got dressed, got to work, came home in the evening, enjoyed themselves, went to bed. On a 60-hour week you can't ask them to go shopping or do the cooking, so each mess had its own mess staff. They were given a cooked breakfast before they left, they were given a packed lunch, they were given a cooked meal when they came home – well, tea if they got home about 5, a cooked meal in the evening. In the main mess they had a choice of three starters, etc. We all lived well. Grand Met looked after us: your bed was made, your room was cleaned, all you had to do was undress and go to bed. Every mess had a swimming pool and small gym, everybody had transport. We had the usual problems in Saudi: forty or fifty men living together, wanting to arrange dances with the nurses' home – and that did get me into trouble, I must admit.

I called it the Animal Farm: it was a mess not far from where we were. The mess manager called, saying, 'We've got police parked outside, we're going to be raided.' And I said, 'What's the position?' He said, 'We have a dozen nurses here.' It was a Thursday night dance, actually. I said, 'You've

Learning the trade in the Arabian Gulf

got to go dry. If my memory serves me correctly, you've got sixteen toilets in each block, you've got two swimming pools, sixteen baths, and six kitchens. It's dead easy to get rid of it.' They rang back about an hour later and said, 'We're nearly OK.' I said, 'Is there anyone still missing from the mess?' They said, 'Yes, two riggers, we don't know where they are.' And one of them then came bouncing down the road. Now, the police wouldn't raid you: they had to have somebody open the door. And what did this rigger do? He opened the door, saw the police car there, they ran to the front door, so they were in. I had eight guys arrested that night: one of them was found in a water tank upstairs on the roof, trapped in the water tank. He'd left his shoes outside ...

And the new Chief Executive and General Manager were flying in that evening to take over the project. What a start!

It was an enormous country, and we were supplying the Saudi National Guard with a total communications system. If you regard the National Guard as the Royal Family's private army, that's what we were involved in. The types of people we employed were very unusual from the Cable & Wireless point of view, because you had 'holes and poles' men, digging holes and putting poles in; you had Diesel Dans, diesel generator people. In normal circumstances they would all be national staff locally recruited, you wouldn't be involved with them. There were some rogues amongst them, absolute rogues, but you learnt a lot ... On my trips, I had to visit all the messes regularly. That's where I came up against those who'd never been abroad before. Some had come from unemployment situations, especially ex-Merchant Navy. Diesel generator guys (because we ran our own power supplies down there as well), people we would not normally employ but we needed their skill. Then there were teachers who taught English as a foreign language, but you were teaching basically Bedu tribesmen how to become technicians. I think they had a far harder time than I did in that sense.

John Davenport, *working in Doha in the Arabian Gulf in the early 1970s, and based in Bahrain for a considerable period of time, had somewhat different experiences with alcohol in nations where Muslim law held sway.*

It was quite a big roost because we ran the Qatar National Telephone Service in addition to providing the international telecommunications, so I had about probably fifty or more foreign service staff and a much larger total workforce and I was the interface with the government for both the national telephone service and the international. So, yes, it was challenging. Job satisfying. Doha was a bit of a strange place, lacking in amenities but again we made the most of it. All the children learned to sail and water-ski there – and I learned something about the import and sale of alcoholic beverages.

Liquor was licensed, you got – if you had a licence – a certain amount; and the government chose to nominate a limited number of concerns to run what it called liquor syndicates. The oil company ran a liquor syndicate, and they chose Cable & Wireless to run a liquor syndicate. And as Doha developed – and it did develop very rapidly while we were there – there was an influx of contractors and civil engineers and all sorts of people like that. A number of syndicates grew up, and then the government was unhappy with some of them because it was felt they were selling liquor to the Arabs. So they shut down all of them except Cable & Wireless and the oil company. By this time, Cable & Wireless were left servicing a large population of expatriates and turning over in excess of £2 million a year. And this was all meant to be run as a non-profit-making organisation, and originally run by a Cable & Wireless employee in his spare time. But of course by this time that had become impossible, so we had somebody fully employed running the liquor syndicate with a committee which I chaired sitting over the top of him ... And somehow money was just growing in the bank account. It was incredible ... It's typical of my life with Cable & Wireless. I mean, what's that got to do with telecommunications – running a legal alcohol syndicate?

Richard Histed *spent a total of ten years in the Philippines. The new coaxial cable systems that were criss-crossing the Pacific and South-East Asia region in the 1970s were among his primary responsibilities. (He later took on business development throughout South-East Asia and spearheaded Cable & Wireless's moves in the course of the 1980s into both Macao and Japan.) It was a far smaller enterprise than was happening in the Gulf and Saudi Arabia, but satisfying both governments and native peoples proved to be just as difficult.*

When we were building the coaxial cable station, we were told by President Marcos, who came from the province where we were putting the cable station in, that we had to employ local labour. Adjacent to us there was this fishing village which I suppose had 30 or 40 people who were employable as labourers. And so the first week, they turned up. The other thing was they had to be paid at Manila wages. So at the end of the week, they got their money, and went home. Monday morning, nobody turned up. I went down to the village, and there they all were, absolutely blind drunk, as indeed they had been ever since they got their money. They hadn't had so much money before, because what we'd given them in a week was what they'd earn in three or four months.

The big thing was that the village really worked on a barter system: they fished, they bartered their fish for rice, for pigs, this, that and the other, and that's how they earned a living. The fishermen hadn't been out fishing, so they had nothing to barter with, so they'd got no food, and the wives and the children were suffering. The wives then came to us and said, 'Please *don't* employ our men. The men won't make any complaints, and we will find a way.' At the height, we had about three or four hundred workers on the site, and the wives set up little stalls where they sold lunch and food to the workers, and in fact, in the end most of our workers did come from Manila. Although we were supposed to employ these local people, it just destroyed the local economy because it really was a barter system – but the wives, by selling the food, could get sufficient money to augment what they were doing. And the men didn't have the money, so they didn't drink, and they had to go and fish. And everything in the garden was rosy.

Market colour in Bahrain, one of Cable & Wireless's longest-established stations in the Arabian Gulf

Submarine telephone cable off the coast of Bermuda

Richard Selby *found himself in the late 1970s in one of the many new territories that Cable & Wireless was taking on, North Yemen. Before he joined Cable & Wireless he had considered a career in broadcasting: there he had his heart's desire, of sorts.*

We went off to North Yemen, up in the mountains, and my goodness, it was dreadful. It was certainly an eye opener, even for me. By then I'd had my first introduction to the Arab world ... but I think I was probably unprepared for Sana'a. (North Yemen and South Yemen in those days were two different countries.)

To start with, my new wife and I lived above the Company office. We had a block of flats, a four-storey block: the ground floor and the first two floors were equipment rooms, the engineering floor, and the offices, and we were right on the top of the building. They called it the transit flat where people went in transit, and we were part of an expanding staff number, so Cable & Wireless had to go out and rent another mansion for us to live in. A villa, a little villa. Things in Yemen were not easy to come by, furnishing and so on, so Cable & Wireless used to rely on buying a house furnishing kit. This was something that must have been well established, a standard kit one of the big companies in London put together, and would freight. By the time our villa was available, the furnishing kit hadn't arrived, so various members of staff contributed a plate, a cup, a knife, and we ended up with enough cups and knives and forks to survive. Then this furnishing kit arrived, three great boxes full of all sorts of things ... There was a time when Cable & Wireless had Cable & Wireless etched into their knives. But it wasn't like having Cable & Wireless tattooed into the back of your neck ...

Cable & Wireless had a contract in those days with the Ministry of Communications to operate and maintain their radio broadcasting studios and their medium wave broadcasting transmitter for Radio Sana'a ... When I got to Yemen and the transmitting station, the broadcasting transmitter was Czechoslovakian, with enormous great generators made by Skoda, but they were marine engines. Ship's engines, enormous great things. The studios themselves

The Cable & Wireless counter in Sana'a

were in the city centre, and they were all equipped with Chinese equipment. All this equipment was given to Yemen: the Chinese had donated the hulking great tape recorders and the console, and the Czechs had given the other bits. Maintenance manuals? There weren't that many and what there were weren't written in fluent English by any means. But we managed to keep it up and running. We survived a change of government. That was a bit difficult because some of the soldiers cut out the control desk on one occasion because they didn't want anything transmitted not going through them, but it was returned eventually and re-cabled in.

Chris Schofield *had been in Yemen a year or two before, and had a very difficult time of it.*

Yes, if you went out at night, not that there were many places to go to, you would suddenly be held up on the road and told to go back from where you came. One never knew what they were doing beyond that area: they said they were moving guns and things, you just didn't get to see. Where we lived, in the compound behind the office, we were next door to the Chinese compound. There they had barbed wire all the way round and arc lights on all night long; a bloke wandered round our area, I was never quite certain whether he was employed by them or by us. You didn't really know. You felt that any one of the staff if they got niggled with you could give information, and if you were taken away that was it, nobody could do anything about it, you were powerless, because there was no real organisation. The Consul ... Well, yes, he was there, he was very sociable, we had parties there, and BP round the corner, they were all living fairly normal lives, but we at Cable & Wireless seemed to be rather fighting the local. They wanted us to provide a service, and didn't want to pay for anything ... It wasn't nice, I didn't like that, and the family wasn't there. You had chats on the phone just once a month, and neither of us were terribly happy about that.

Ian Corrall *found himself over the years in many difficult and forlorn locations. A posting with an easy life could be overturned by a telephone call and an airline ticket.*

I went to Turks and Caicos Islands next. I was Assistant Engineer there. It was a radio station, we also had cables. The Company had bought the old NASA range cable and diverted it a bit, because there was a NASA tracking station on Grand Turk; we bought their old cable and brought it ashore in various places to run telephones on the Islands. Spent a lot of time tweaking that up, but it was done for a few quid. A local joke was I spent more time in an airplane flying up and down this cable than I did on the ground, but I was only there for six or seven months, and I got pulled out to do the satellite station in the Maldive Islands.

Two years there: they were going to make it three. It's an island a mile square. 140 islands in the chain. Not an easy place to live in … The big problem was food: fish and that was it.

I had a medical when I was there and the doctor said, 'You're suffering from malnutrition!' We discussed it, and he said, 'Well, the local people live on fish and rice, but they've been doing it for generations.' And there was very little stuff to get there: from Ceylon Airways, the old Ceylon line, the cabin crews used to come in with big plastic bags of vegetables which they used to sell; also from the Ceylon Cold Store. We ended up, later on, myself and this Australian bloke, setting up an operation to import foodstuffs from Singapore, and to include the stuff imported from Ceylon Cold Store.

There were only two of us running the station technically, and only one of us could go off the island at a time. A crowd of people would get together, we'd hire a boat, and go off to one of the resort islands on a Sunday, but one always had to stay behind. So it meant you could only get off the island once a fortnight – and if you didn't go off that once a fortnight you knew about it! There were over 30,000 people on that island. The UN people said 'It's not viable, it shouldn't work. It does, but it shouldn't.'

CORPORATE CHANGE AND THE ECLIPSE OF F1

In a changing communications world, with changing political orders, and a vastly different commercial environment, Cable & Wireless experienced tremendous upheaval over the 1960s and 1970s. The old dominance of the London Head Office was gradually eroded. The style and type of people employed in London changed as definitively as did those overseas. Many of the large-scale British expatriate communities had vanished, and the F1 way of life was going with them. Improvements in pay and conditions had to be set alongside wider employment of short-term staff and the erosion of the system of three- and four-year 'tours' overseas. New management techniques were embraced with varying degrees of enthusiasm. The traditional male dominance diminished considerably, as did the old hierarchical structure.

Pamela Aylmore *was a path-breaker, in that she rose through the ranks of the Head Office staff, forging ahead in a way that no woman before her had been able to do. She often found resistance.*

When I joined the Company I thought, 'Great, I've always wanted to travel' – and that was to be the biggest joke in my life, because I didn't travel until 1978 and I'd joined in 1944. Although I had various good ideas, when they had to be put out abroad a gentleman had to do it because Cable & Wireless didn't think a young lady should travel on her own.

Everything I did, I was the first woman. It didn't matter what it was. I became the first lady Chief Clerk, in 1972. Every time I went anywhere and did anything, it was me and men right throughout my career. From credit cards, I took on budgets and forecasting: the traffic department was split and became a commercial department, and that was split again and it became public service sales, that again was split and it became sales and marketing. And this is how my life progressed through it, I was always the first lady who'd ever done it ...

In 1966 when the World Cup football was on, we were going to be very busy, and I was laying plans because we had something like nearly 3,500 press correspondents coming from overseas, and they were all going to need credit cards. They phoned me up from the International Football Association to ask if I'd like to go to the press conference. I said, 'Yes, I would very much like to meet them all.' I came in on that particular morning, which was 4 July, very nicely turned out, a black suit, a pretty hat on, ready to go to Wembley. And the phone rang. 'Is that Miss Aylmore? You received an invitation to go to the press conference today?' I said, 'Yes, I did,' and he said, 'Well, I'm sorry, I've been told I must withdraw it because you'd be the only lady amongst 3,500 men, so could you ...' – this was 1966 – '... so could you send a male representative instead?' I said, 'Well. We don't happen to have one in the credit card section, we're all ladies, every one of us. So you'll just have to go along without us.'

Pat Cowan, *while working in London, could see the extent of the change in the Company and in telecommunications that occurred in the first half of the 1970s.*

The early seventies saw a very, very large technology change. The real move to wide-band, to international dialling. Telex was on a high, message-switching for airlines and banks and people like this – it was all new technology. Computers coming in. And then there were the billing systems. That was the period when we were starting looking around for talent: we started up Asiadata in Hong Kong, and brought in someone from ICL to run it. People said, 'Why are you bringing in people from outside to run the computer systems?' – because we'd always tended to do this ourselves, you know, but it needed the specialisation. There was just so much going on. It was a very large growth area. There was the problem of having to bring in a lot of outsiders, at high cost, wages that were beginning to make people say, 'Why are you paying that person that amount?' So there was wholesale change; that period between 1970 and 1974 was a big change, and I think, working in London, there were a lot of people that weren't totally happy with what was going on.

Jim Bairstow, *who was recruited in his native Australia in the TELCOM days of the Second World War, remains philosophical about the F1 way of life that he joined thereafter.*

I'm still searching for something in my career that was outstanding, but I was inclined – and I think the majority of people were inclined – to regard it as a mobile life, and you took things as they came. Some postings were good, some were better – and some you'd rather not know about. But my wife and I very early on adopted a philosophy. We would not argue about a posting. If one came, we would take it. There were some who would argue the toss about it. And having come to that agreement we stuck to it, and I can't really say that *any* place we went, there weren't some factors that were rewarding.

Joan Sherwood *reflects on the continuing bond between people who have led an expatriate lifestyle.*

I think there's a special bond between expatriates. You're used to the same lifestyle, whereas I used to find going back to England when we visited my brother and that, they're regimented basically, lunch is a certain time, dinner's a certain time. Whereas when you live overseas you eat when you feel like it, if you meet somebody or people come to you everything is so casual, you do things when you want to do them, it's a much more relaxed style. And I think while a lot of our friends here are expats, we're used to that type of life, and we get on together so well because this is the life you have led, and you have so much in common. There are a lot of people here – I'm not being snobbish at all – but who have never left Australia and you find that you are inhibited about talking to them about the way you have lived because you feel that you're showing off, and it isn't, because that's been your life, and they're not part of that whereas with other expats you talk about where you've been and it's just part of conversation. You gel together.

John Worrall *left the mobile expatriate workforce to teach at, and ultimately be Principal of, the Cable & Wireless College at Porthcurno. He retired when the College moved to its new home in Coventry.*

The foreign service life had changed [by the end of the 1970s]: there were more and more short tours, unaccompanied tours of three to six months. Not these leisurely three-year postings, when you took your family with you and had a nice time. It was very much more business-like. By this time we were being privatised, it was all change, more dynamic, not so laid-back. We're here to provide a service and that's all that counts. Profit was the order of the day, efficiency and all those things, accountability.

Even though it's changed and has to respond much more rapidly to market needs, Cable & Wireless has still got that feel of a smaller company. Whereas if you worked for, say, British Telecom, the AT&Ts, those really huge concerns, you really can't feel part of much more than your local unit. Here you do feel part of a global empire. Because of places like Porthcurno, and the College at Coventry at the moment, you're actually in contact with the world-wide work force much of the time, moving around. Yes, there still is that family feel about it. Whether it will continue to last as it gets bigger and bigger, I don't know.

Brenda Histed, *who accompanied her husband in many parts of the world, principally in South America and South-East Asia including a ten-year stint in the Philippines, still found that a life abroad offered scope for adventures that she might otherwise never have dreamed of.*

I met this Father George who was a Catholic priest in Manila, and he was learning the dialect to go up north ... When we went on one of these trips to the coaxial cable station, I went on further still to see Father George. He had said to me, one day, 'Do you want to go with the missionaries?' I said I'd love to, so off we went with a water buffalo and this sled with a generator on, and we went up the mountainside. We had to hump this generator up there because they were going to show pictures of Jesus, and at the top of the hill were all these little tiny flat-nosed people, shaking my hand and touching my nose, they thought it was wonderful.

We were showing these projected slides of Jesus, and all the kids were running behind and seeing what was behind this thing. They'd never seen anything like it in their lives. They lived in little grass huts. Then we were packing up about two hours later, and all of a sudden there was a whole row of Kalingas, people with beads and rings through their noses. They'd seen this light, and they'd literally walked two hours to see what was happening. So we said OK, and we had to show it all over again. Couldn't say, 'I'm sorry the show's over,' so we had the slide show over again.

It was about 11.30 or 12 by the time we finished, and I can remember walking down this mountain. It was one of those silver nights, and the stillness around. And the sound of the forest: it was so noisy, with all these insects. It was like an out of body experience. I looked down and I'd got my red espadrilles on, and I thought, 'Wouldn't Marks & Spencer be amazed to know where these shoes had gone?'

The next afternoon I went along the river in a dugout canoe to see some of the villagers. I sat in the middle of this dugout canoe with a black umbrella, because the nuns said it's so very hot, and I thought, 'Is this really me?' I kept pinching myself. They were giving me these alcoholic drinks they make, that I was drinking out of seashells, and I thought, 'Oh well, it's very good, and it'll kill any germs, I'm sure.'

I feel very privileged to have met Father George who took me to see all these wonderful things. They're the little treasures you get amongst the sadness and the illness.

NATIONALISED, PRIVATISED

Cable & Wireless had been one of the enterprises that had passed into public ownership under the post-1945 Labour government. It became the sleeping giant thereafter, little-known at home because almost all its commercial activities were overseas, and frequently left to its own devices by successive governments. Cable & Wireless was to become one of the first publicly owned enterprises to be returned to private ownership under the post-1979 Conservative government. With privatisation – a word virtually unknown when the Company was released from public control in 1981 – many of the commercial forces that had been making their presence felt in the 1970s were unleashed. It was a cathartic experience, and the end of that story is still unfolding.

George Warwick *was one of many who felt frustrated in the publicly owned Cable & Wireless of the 1960s that the Treasury set cash limits and that the Company's bureaucracy was closely entangled with that of Government.*

We had trouble in every respect with the telex service [in Hong Kong]. It was semi-automatic when I got there, and the switch wasn't big enough. We had two problems getting that bigger: one was manufacturing delays, because you could order something and it would take three or four years before you got it, particularly from the UK. Remember I'm talking about the 1960s, late 1960s. And the other thing was getting London to agree with it: it would take them six months to a year to agree to something you wanted yesterday.

It used to have to go to every department in Head Office, and they could take months over it. Then it had to go to a special Board meeting. I think they held one every three months or something to discuss capital. Then it had to go to the Department of Trade and Industry, unless it was a small amount. That could take another three months. That was before you could place the order. And, at that time, we were almost forced to order from British suppliers, who would accept the order and deliver when they felt like it and it could take two or three years sometimes ...

We got into trouble on one occasion, because London were saying there just weren't any teleprinters available. So [one of the staff] bought six hundred in Australia. They weren't quite exactly the standard ones: they worked perfectly all right as a telex, but the keyboard was slightly different. Does it matter? We did get a lot of people connected up to telex. Those machines paid for themselves within two months of being put in, and from then on of course it was gravy.

Paul Carrington, *as the first local employee to become a General Manager within the Company, was the prototype for many who followed. He had joined in the war years as an operator in Barbados, and only ever worked in the Caribbean.*

When I joined the Company, your one ambition in life was to provide a prompt service and a reasonably good service, a reliable service. That seemed almost an impossibility in the days of HF radio, when you had atmospheric conditions and all sorts of other things working against you. But we've been able to achieve that – and now the biggest challenge is to try and anticipate the market. So in the past, where you were behind the market, trying to provide what you knew the market would want, now you're in a position where you've done that and you ask, what can we provide next?

George Warwick *retired from the Company just as its privatisation was taking place. Hong Kong, where he had been General Manager and where these sorts of questions had often been asked, had long been by far the most profitable element in the whole of the Company.*

Very cosy it was, but then it was a nationalised company, the shareholder wasn't breathing down anybody's neck. As far as I can make out the shareholder's requirement was 'Don't come to us for any money.' Right up to

Barbados: earth station, sea and sky

the late 1960s or 1970s we were capitalised at £50 million; Archie Willett, who was Managing Director from 1973 to 1977, got that increased by a share split to £100 million – for a company that when it went on the market was, what, £800 million. Actually, the Cable & Wireless group was sold for roughly what Hong Kong was worth, if you look at the figures.

Patricia Bosdet *was Project Manager for privatisation. It was a novelty for everybody concerned, whether in Whitehall, the Cable & Wireless Head Office, or in the locations overseas.*

With Cable & Wireless's privatisation, free shares were given to employees. The Government was keen to do this, and they set aside an amount of shares to give to employees. The particular complication was you had to check the tax requirement in all of the locations around the world. There was a little team of lawyers, who were contacting people all over the globe, saying, 'What are the tax implications of handing out free shares?' A lot of it was done through trusts set up to hold a block of shares in those countries, and then hand them out. The amounts were relatively small, in the UK it was £200 perhaps. If you hand out a block of free shares or the cash equivalent of those shares, in some of the smaller locations where Cable & Wireless operated, it was a lot of money and it could obviously completely change their life style. You had a lot to think about.

There were logistical problems that affected Cable & Wireless which other companies didn't have. All employees were given the opportunity to apply for shares when the Company was floated in the first place. So if you had had a UK company you would send out the share forms, no problem. But what if you had a cableship which goes out to a cable break in the middle of the sea? You actually had to find out ways as to how you could get these forms to the ship and make sure they had the opportunity to get them back again within the time limit.

Richard Selby *was working abroad when Cable & Wireless's privatisation first came about. His perception of change, like many overseas, was quite different from those who were based in the UK.*

I was working in Saudi on the National Guard Project, and I remember people came from London to tell us we were being privatised and to give us the opportunity to buy shares. Some people said fah, rubbish – and some people hocked themselves up to the hilt and bought as many shares as they could, and made an immediate killing. We didn't *feel* any different, and really it wasn't until I came back to the UK and could see that Mercury was forming and that's when you really felt there was change afoot, and the first time I recognised any change was when I got back to the UK. Overseas I didn't feel the change.

Rod Olsen *arrived in London from South-East Asia in 1987 as Finance Director, and subsequently became Deputy Chief Executive and Acting Chief Executive. He has been intimately involved in the changes of business direction and corporate style within Cable & Wireless.*

There was a big conference in 1976, the year before I joined the Company. A whole bunch of people were gathered from all around the group, to discuss the Company's future. I think everyone recognised the path the Company was on was destined to [fail] ... Life moves on, and we did a lot of things, we *experimented* with a lot of things: we had business systems groups, we were quite successful in doing things in airports, underground railway systems and communications that go with that, project and contract type work. But it was never a mainstream part of what the Company was, and it isn't today ... A lot of dramatic things were going to happen and we were going to have to find new avenues, but there were also people around I believe whose view might have been, 'Well, if that is the case, we should just wind the Company up, put all the money in the pension fund and all go and find something else to do.' There was a hard core opinion around of those sorts of things.

Quite clearly, in 1981 we were hugely, overly, dependent on Hong Kong. That was not a great way to be shaped as a business. So many of the things we did, Mercury in the UK, Japan ... the motivation for all of those things was to spread the risk ... There's an awful lot more to Cable & Wireless now than there was then, and it's still growing.

The stories told by men and women who have been associated with Cable & Wireless take us 'over the horizon' of the globe and of the past. The changes in ownership in 1981 were a real watershed for Cable & Wireless. It was never again to be like the Company it had been. Yet the continuities remain. Continuities in personnel and places, technology and history, hardship and good living, adventure and romance.

CHAPTER SIX

Hong Kong and China

As a place to live, Hong Kong really picks you up and throws you along. I was working for a long time over a hundred hours a week. Still, going out there, you just got carried with it. It was a very dynamic place.

Ian Corrall

Cable & Wireless's involvement with Hong Kong began in 1871 when the first submarine cable reached it. The links through to the Far East, to Hong Kong but also, before the Second World War, to Shanghai, were always the principal element in Cable & Wireless's worldwide communications network. Generations of employees marvelled at the colony's physical setting and were thrilled by its energy. In the course of time, particularly from the 1960s, Hong Kong was to become one of the most dynamic and vibrant of all the Asian economies, and it stood fast against Communist mainland China. In the Company's terms, Hong Kong came to represent an ever-greater proportion of its global business. By the 1960s and 1970s it was the largest of the Cable & Wireless establishments, and the Company had a significant role in the whole infrastructure of the Crown Colony as well as running its external telecommunications. Almost without exception, new technologies were introduced in Hong Kong first, and new business ideas were developed there that animated other parts of Cable & Wireless's world.

Re-establishing links and doing business with China has been a continuing theme of the Company's presence in Hong Kong. In 1997 Hong Kong was returned to China and ceased to be a British Crown Colony; by that time significant steps had been taken over the course of many years to re-cement Cable & Wireless's commercial position and communications strength in China.

Maurice Bane *spent two periods working in Hong Kong. He went there for the first time in 1953, and returned (now with a wife and children) in 1960. Even sailing in on his first visit Hong Kong harbour was a wonder to behold.*

The tannoy said, 'If you want to have your first sight of Hong Kong come up on deck.' I couldn't believe it. This was 1953, there weren't the enormous buildings there at that time, there was very little on the Kowloon side. There was the Peninsular Hotel and the piers with all the ocean liners, and a lot of buildings at the side up the side of the hill there. Yes, I was impressed, because there were the skyscrapers on the island. In those days the Cable & Wireless office building was right on the waterfront, a seven-storey building, and it was numbered among some of the higher ones. The Bank of China was bigger, and we just topped the Hong Kong Club, which we were next to, and then there were more buildings on the waterfront. This was Hong Kong, the Pearl of the Orient ...

Here, for the first time, there was a modern station ... The Central Telegraph Office was very big, and the radio station was very big too. We'd taken over the combined services there: the police, radio services and other things ... So we had a big radio transmitting station, a big radio receiving station, and all this fed into the control room in the building, and we had underground cables which connected everything on the hillside and away across the island.

Even in those early days, there was a pulse about Hong Kong: it was alive, people moved rapidly in the streets, and people were working very hard. There wasn't a great deal of room for laconic people who just drifted around, people worked hard ... Hong Kong was so vibrant. You'd look across the harbour, because our office was right on the waterfront, and the harbour was always so alive, the ferry going back and forth, junks were sailing through, big ships were coming in. You'd see a great liner coming in, and the moving around of the tugs, then a grey cruiser. American ships. The harbour was always so alive, I can't see that you could ever find it dull there. But it had to come to an end, so eventually I was relieved ...

Hong Kong at night

We sailed in on the *Hamburg*, and Mary and I were shattered. We were up on deck to see it, and we said, 'Golly, how long have we been away?' About three years, maybe three and a half. We couldn't believe it, on the right hand side, in Kowloon, tenement buildings had all gone up. You couldn't recognise the island front. You couldn't pick out the Cable & Wireless building, because its little seven floors were completely dominated by a large hotel of twenty floors alongside it. The Hong Kong & Shanghai Bank had gone way up, Chartered Bank had gone way up, and the Bank of China was going up as well – had to be taller than any of them ...

The Company was stretched quite a lot, because we ran all the news agencies and we were into [private leased telex] circuits in a big way, business had recognised this was the money spinner. Telex was booming, like mad, we couldn't really cope at one time with the telex customers. We were running things like PanAm signal centre, and they based the whole of their Asian system out to India and onwards to the Middle East, that and their communications centre in Hong Kong. The revenue from that venture alone was absolutely tremendous. Radio Hong Kong. Traffic control systems. We were making money hand over fist, I suppose Hong Kong was contributing about 60 per cent of the Company's revenue. By then we had lost Singapore, and quite a few other places, so it really was the Jewel in the Crown ...

Ian Corrall *served in possibly more parts of the world than any other recent employee of the Company. Despite that, his direct contact with disasters was limited. He was, however, in Hong Kong in 1966.*

I was there in this famous flood in Hong Kong: tremendous storm, 67-odd people drowned. It was on a Sunday and I was actually going to go to work, but the mountain behind us was just a mass of waterfalls.

It was a cyclone really. It rained, it had been raining for several days, but what happened around 7 or 8 o'clock in the morning, six inches of rain fell. I said, 'I'm not going to work in this,' and Bob Bruce who ran the airline communications centre said, 'Well, *I'm* going in, I've got some work to do,' and he got down the road, but the whole mountain was coming across the road, and that was that ... Being a Sunday there weren't too many people about. This is the sort of thing. Cars at the side of the road. Statistically they reckon once every five hundred years. We were lucky: if it had been a weekday there would have been thousands dead.

Howard Kleyn *had a number of responsibilities in Hong Kong, the most important being the range of special services that Cable & Wireless provided there* *(see pp 193–4).*

When I first went to Hong Kong in 1967 it was still very much Chinese, although British-administered for the past century or whatever it was, nevertheless ... If you wandered through Central Square you could still see women wearing cheong-sams, and there was even the odd pigtail as well, and the little Chinese skull caps. There were many place names, or street names, written up in Chinese characters. By the time I left, which was eight and a half years later, that had virtually disappeared entirely. The girls you saw around the Central district at lunch time, typists, people like that, they were wearing western dresses, and it looked just like a London park might do on a summer's day. Most notices by that time were in English, although of course they had Chinese alongside, but it had all become very much westernised during that period I was there. When I went there it was really Chinese, when I came away it was Anglo-Chinese.

Wendy Suart, *who had felt very isolated when stationed in Hong Kong previously* *(pp 85–6)**, had decided that as the General Manager's wife in the late 1960s and early 1970s it was incumbent upon her to do something for the wives and families of Cable & Wireless's expatriate employees.*

CHANHUNGNAI TAILOR
鏞記酒家
梁金齡
CHAN
MODERN TAILOR
Photo

Eventually we built up a highly complex system of activities for the wives. I worked on the principle that if a wife was happy the husband would work better. If he comes home every night to a whining, complaining wife and how she hates Hong Kong and how lonely she is and how miserable she is, you know he's going to lose confidence in his work, and think, 'Oh God, perhaps I'd better ask for a transfer.' So I determined to keep the wives happy. We had badminton on a Monday, we'd have a Red Cross gathering once a month on Tuesdays when we'd do good works like bandage rolling and things. Once in three months we'd have a blood bank and collect blood, once a month on a Wednesday we'd have the coffee party, and then once a month on Thursday we would have outings ...

We combed Hong Kong. We did trips round the New Territories, we did trips to the jade carving factory, we did trips to the camphorwood chest manufactory. There was a wonderful towel factory which sold seconds: we took our shoes off and climbed all over these great piles of reject towels and picked out good ones. And we went to a huge housing estate which was bigger than anything in Europe and were taken over that. We went to the leprosy island where leprosy patients were kept; we went to a drug withdrawal centre in Wanchai. And I kept looking for new places – a wonderful haute couture place ... Or a sweat shop in Kowloon city, climbing up to the third floor of a tenement building, where they would have seconds in jumpers or woollen things, and coming home laden with goodies.

Ron Werngren *oversaw the introduction of the first International Maintenance Centre.*

Hong Kong? Fabulous. You felt you were at the centre of the universe. It lived off trading so the newspaper had news from all over the world. The first flat we had, on the middle of the island, not very high up, we looked south over Aberdeen Harbour. You know these Chinese paintings where typically there's a hill and a cloud halfway up: almost every

A bustling Hong Kong street of the early 1960s

morning, you had something like that. You had an amah who lived in, did the cooking, baby-sitting, cleaning, that sort of thing. We said to each other, 'This is a dying thing, let's enjoy it while we can.' We lived in flats, but the flat was four bedrooms, three living rooms, verandah: very, very spacious. You looked out onto the hillside, but because we were overlooking Aberdeen, we were overlooking a water catchment area, there were no buildings. It was all very green.

Then we moved to just the other side of the crest, to the harbour side of the central ridge. The harbour is incredible. In those days it had A buoys and B buoys, something like 24 A buoys and 26 B buoys. They'd be full, full of ocean-going ships. Movement all the time. The paper would carry shipping news: who had come in, where they were going. Busy-ness, but not the frantic state it is now. The last time I was there, 1992, I wouldn't have wanted to live there at all: it's just too frantic, too money grabbing. I'm talking now of 1966 to 1970, that's a long time ago now. There weren't so many people. Still about five million, but we could get out of our first flat and walk a couple of hundred yards onto a contour path and you wouldn't seem to think there'd be another human being around. You can't do that now.

Brian Pemberton *moved to Hong Kong from a successful period in private business systems, one of the new range of opportunities opened up from the late 1960s. Ultimately he was the member of the Company's board with responsibility for Hong Kong.*

You lived on the edge of your experience, your nerves. It was everything. It's the most stimulating place to work, I would guess, other than maybe New York. Because of the drive of the Hong Kong Chinese, they're the most magnificent people to work with. You think, 'Oh, how the hell are we going to do this?' Then you sit down and talk it through. It was what I call Noproblemsville. You say, 'We're going to do so and so, is this going to be a problem?' 'No, no problem.'

Tropospheric scatter aerials, Cape d'Aguilar, Hong Kong in 1968

That's why I think some people who've lived there all their lives get a 'walk on water' syndrome, they think it's them that's done it whereas in actual fact, in our case, it was I believe 17,000 people. We've done it, you might have had the happy chance of being there at the time it happened. They're great people.

Rod Olsen *first went to Hong Kong from his native New Zealand in 1971. He returned there as Cable & Wireless's newly appointed Branch Accountant in 1978. Even greater change was in the air, as Cable & Wireless acquired more significant business in the Crown Colony while at home privatisation would soon change Cable & Wireless for ever.*

Cable & Wireless in Hong Kong was never intimately a part of the Hong Kong scene. If you looked at the Hong Kong Bank or Jardines, they were described as Hongs in Hong Kong: you would expect to see a Jardine person or a Bank person on the Legislative Council, the Executive Council. Cable & Wireless was never that much integrated into the way of things in Hong Kong, it stood slightly aside from all that. So we never have had our representatives in the organs of government bodies in Hong Kong – that I think was wise, not to get that close. We had licences which caused us to keep just a little bit at arm's length, but to do the job very professionally. It's a little different from the other operators, traders and wheeler-dealers in Hong Kong.

I was the guy who had the job of turning the Hong Kong branch into a limited liability company and then preparing it for Cable & Wireless's privatisation in the UK. We had in the year and a half before that a huge dispute with the local telephone company over how much we paid each other, how we shared the revenue for international calls, which came to a head with the telephone company cutting off Cable & Wireless's water, really. They stopped paying us. If you think of the size of Hong Kong in relation to the rest of the group, there was only so long that could go on for before the group had some difficulties, so it eventually went to arbitration.

That then set the stage to enable us to turn it into a company, and move ahead to privatisation. We sold the Hong Kong government 20 per cent of it. I still have a photocopy of the cheques which the government gave us. The original cheque couldn't be processed by the bank because their computers didn't have enough zeroes.

Pat Cowan *spent much of the 1980s in Hong Kong, and subsequently opened Cable & Wireless's first office in Beijing.*

Hong Kong was exciting from a telecoms point of view. I suppose everything was growing with it. From a telecoms point of view there was everything there, Hong Kong was becoming a key part of the world network. We were being listened to in international forums. I was involved very much in the whole of the future Pacific planning, which was the new fibre-optics systems around the Pacific. By the time I arrived there in 1979 we were almost coming to the end of the analogue era and were moving into the digital era. So it was very exciting to be there from 1979 through to 1986 when the whole went digital, everything moved from analogue to digital and we had to replace all our equipment to cope with that. The expansion of the network was phenomenal. I went there just as we grew to a thousand circuits through the satellite network. By the time I left there was something like seven thousand circuits.

We were growing at a phenomenal rate. We were beginning to expand into China, and we did a lot of work with China to do that. But all that couldn't have been done without the foresight of people who had been in Hong Kong before, and built up and got relationships with Taiwan, the relationship with China, relationship with Japan, which had been a difficult growing period. And to make Hong Kong key, and to keep it one above Singapore.

Fung Hak Ming *entered the world of telecommunications as a boy when the Japanese were occupying Hong Kong, and then joined Cable & Wireless when* *peace came. He rose from the lowliest of positions to become the first local-born person to occupy senior posts within Cable & Wireless's Hong Kong operations, eventually becoming Managing Director. He attributes his skills to the efficacy of prayer as much as to his native talent, as on one occasion when he was assured by expatriate engineers that an installation was exactly as the manual said it should be.*

Maybe it was fine but it still didn't work. So I prayed. I still could not cure the fault, so I thought, 'Well, I have to pray again.' And after I prayed, I looked down and I saw a wire that was missing, so I put it back. And put it all back to normal.

Then they invited Princess Anne to inaugurate the second earth station. From the General Manager down to the technicians, everyone was so excited that Princess Anne was coming. So that nothing should go wrong, we kept on rehearsing all the time, how to do everything. When that morning came, and I was participating in the ceremony, I only spent ten minutes in my office. I was so calm. Nothing went wrong. After that ceremony, the European staff asked me, 'How come you were so calm?' I said, 'Because I prayed before the ceremony. It's not me, it's God. He got me through.'

So when I have any problem I pray and I always solve all my problems. That is how it was from when I was an apprentice and promoted right up to Managing Director in the course of forty-two years. I was MD for four years, then I retired. Before retirement I was also participating in the merger of the Hong Kong Telephone Company with Cable & Wireless. In Hong Kong it has all become one company under Hong Kong Telecom ...

In the late 1980s the Company wanted to localise all the senior posts, and it was far easier then than before. In the early 1970s even, and the 1960s of course, those who were locally trained and educated were not up to the international standard, but from the 1980s we employed staff who had studied abroad for three or four years, and things were different. In some cases, their English was even better than some of the UK staff! In 1967 we had riots in Hong Kong and some people sent their children to study abroad. When they came back, their English was up to international standard, so we began to get very good, local English-speaking staff.

So some good things came out of the disturbances.

With all that, the most enjoyable part of my career with Cable & Wireless was the satellite earth station. Stanley Earth Station. That was a golden time in my life with Cable & Wireless. A lot of new things were coming up all the time, and you tended to meet people all round the world, at international meetings and things like that, and there was always room for improvement on satellite communication, and I could offer my knowledge to improve things. But the best part was just enjoying life there. I even got a swimming pool, because we had a standby engine in case of power failure (a very old-fashioned government engine), and the engine needed a water tank for cooling. We used it as a swimming pool ourselves, changing the water once every two or three days, and then later on we put small tropical fish down in there. During Chinese New Year when people throw fire crackers, and burn the grass, we became fire fighters as well.

A good relationship with China had long been the goal of Cable & Wireless in Hong Kong. The access that was achieved in the 1990s was based upon a long history of visits and collaborative ventures, some of which were little known at the time.

John Rippengal *was one of the linchpins in Hong Kong in the 1960s, as Manager International Relations. He spent a very considerable part of his career in, and based in, the Crown Colony.*

Arthur Wood, the General Manager, was the guy who first broke the ice with China in the 1960s. I went with him to China in 1964. We went to tell them about the SEACOM cable which was coming across the Pacific from Guam and linking up with COMPAC Australia. We kept on saying we'd like to come and see you about this and that, and they invited us to come. We went first of all to Canton, and Shanghai. We told them what we wanted, to say 'We want more communication to Shanghai, we want more communication to Canton.' They said, 'Oh no, can't talk about that; you'd better go to Peking.' So we went there. But they were very nice – I said, 'Oh, if we have to go to Peking, I shall miss being able to go to the West Lake at Hang Chow.' They said, 'OK, we'll put you on the train there, you can have a weekend there, and then we'll fly you to Peking,' and that's what they did.

Every morning they'd take us to a diesel factory, or a silk factory, or a museum, to demonstrate the wonders of Chairman Mao. We went to theatres in the evening where they had little sketches of people making carpets in Tibet being flogged by their feudal masters, and then the Communists came and they were all singing songs. 'I can see a glow in the sky. Is it the sun? No, it's the reflection of Chairman Mao.' We did the Summer Palace and all that.

Arthur Wood was the guy. I prodded him a bit as well, because we had the most ridiculous crummy little communication with China. We had one little radio telegraph circuit to Shanghai and a six-channel telephone circuit to Canton, which used to be boosted to twelve during Chinese New Year when everybody went there. We had a good time in a way.

It was Christmas Eve, I always remember. We were sitting in an English restaurant in a Peking hotel, and we were followed around. Wherever we were there were two Russians, and these guys turned up in the hotel too, they were sitting there. Arthur and I were sitting there having a beer about 7 o'clock before dinner, and there were three Japanese sitting at the next table. I looked over and one of these Japanese was crying. The tears were running down his face. I said, 'What's the matter with you?' 'Oh,' he said, 'I'm a Christian, and it's Christmas Day tomorrow and also it's my little girl's third birthday and worst of all I've been in Peking six weeks.' It was a pretty horrible place to be, especially then. I said, 'Oh, why don't you come and join us and have a few beers?' So they came over, and then the Russians were looking and *they* came over. And there was a huge great folk dancing and ballet group from Cuba there, and they all joined us. We had a most marvellous party. It really came home to me, the only common language between all these disparate people, including the Chinese waiters, was English. Nobody ever attempted to speak to anybody else except in English. It really brought home to me what an advantage it was to be born with that as a mother tongue and how universal it had become.

Ted Amor *was at the sharp end of this spirit of cooperation, and his technical expertise brought him into one of the first significant ventures with mainland China.*

I got landed with the Hong Kong coaxial cable system. Hong Kong-Canton ... It was an international circuit so it had to be notified to the International Telecommunications Union in Geneva, and we commissioned it to the date, which is always a feather in your cap with the ITU: you announce that it's coming in, and out of that came the Hong Kong-Canton Railway signalling system.

They had a tatty old cable which had been looked after by Hong Kong Telephone Company not very well at all. It was leaky as blazes, always saturated with water, and they asked Cable & Wireless if we could provide a signalling cable. So we did a little bit of footwork, and said, 'Right, we want the wayleave for the Canton coaxial along the railway. Please. If you can give us wayleave at a peppercorn rent, we will place a second duct while we're laying for you, and provide and install the cable for free.' So that was a good deal. I ended up in charge of this lot too, which meant I had a free pass on the railway. I could wander up and down to the border and back, went into China, and had my own train on one occasion. Distributing [cable] drums along the route.

The cable usually comes in kilometre drums, and when we put in the Canton coax, we'd taken the cable up the road, and in towards the railway through the little lanes. I thought, this is a waste of time, so I had a word with the General Manager of the railway, with the result that we had all the drums dumped at a central point at Shatin, and I took the train out one night. Engine, staff car and low loaders. We distributed at night the cable from top to bottom, all along the railway. Of course, the staff car was well supplied with the usual goodies ... We had this train to ourselves. Marvellous, playing trains: most people had model railways and I had a real one.

The railway signalling system was the old batten, single track rail, signalled up between each station. One station would signal the next one, the token would be delivered, and they would hand in the token. The signalling equipment was extremely bulky, and dated from about 1880; it was all made in Calcutta by the Indian State Railways. We had to design the cables to make this stuff work, and it took amperes and amperes to get those relays over and we had to get special cable for it. That was very successful when it went in. There were all sorts of things to deal with, like treadle switches where the train went over and signalled it was coming up.

When we were laying this cable, Eric Vincent and I were invited up to Canton. We went up by train to the border, to the last station, then we were taken from there to Canton by motor car. We arrived somewhere about 11 or half past in the morning, and they took us to a hotel, gave us a room, because they were sure we'd need some sleep after the long trip from Hong Kong. In each room there was an orange and a banana. So we twiddled our thumbs for an hour or so, then they got us and took us to the telephone exchange. And it looked vaguely familiar to me. I took a closer look, and all the tag strips, all the exchange mechanisms had been lifted out of photographs from the Post Office rate book of the 1930s. It had been copied exactly. You might have been in a pre-war Post Office exchange.

This was in Chairman Mao's day, and we never found any animosity at all. And the border guards, quite openly traded a bottle of Mao Tai for a bottle of Scotch, and waved to each other. That's their local spirit. A combination of diesel oil and carbide by the taste of it.

The train across the border to China

Brian Suart, *as General Manager in the early 1970s, was involved in the next step towards an accommodation with mainland China. (This interview was recorded by Radio Hong Kong in 1974.)*

In Hong Kong we have worked with China for many, many years. The development of communication between China and Hong Kong took a big leap [in 1972] when we were asked to visit Canton in the first instance. Our main traffic stream with China has always been Canton, during the [Trade] Fairs when demand is very high indeed. We have had a VHF system operating twelve telephone channels for many years – twenty years ...

We went to Canton to talk about what could be the next step, because we knew there would be an increasing demand. The decision was made to build a cable as the next step, a land cable, a twin coaxial cable between Hong Kong and Canton. We discussed this matter in June 1972 in Canton. Then the authorities came here to Hong Kong in November of 1972 and we carried it to the point where we knew basically what we were going to do, but the details had to be thrashed out. So I then went with one of our chaps from here and two of our chaps from Head Office in London to Peking for a month, in January 1973. By the end of February we had really worked out in detail what we were going to do, how we were going to do it. We jointly agreed to do it in fourteen months, in time for the Spring Fair this year. And indeed we did. By a hair's breadth – everything had to go right, and everybody had to push very hard in order to do it. It was a fairly sizeable system: it is a cable system that will carry three hundred simultaneous telephone conversations. And large quantities of telegrams, telex, facsimile ...

The first time round that a Chinese delegation came, in November 1971, we had eight visitors. Among other things they came to see us at our house. Things were just a little bit formal when they sat down, and our youngest boy arrived back from kindergarten, aged four, and burst into the room like a rocket. Rather like a character out of a James Thurber book. It was a shout of 'I'm here'. He went round the room shaking hands with everybody by holding them by the hand and jumping up and down, instead of moving his hand, and this went down very big. I think he probably contributed a lot to the success of that particular visit.

John Bragg *had been supervised from Hong Kong during his stint in Vietnam (**see pp 150–2**) and was based there for the other business he conducted in South-East Asia until he left the Company thereafter and moved to Australia. He went in as part of the next wave of access to China.*

My first major trip was about 1979, to put a satellite earth station on top of the military museum in Beijing. And of course, people weren't accepted in those days, especially if you were a foreigner, at the military museum. There was a US spy plane outside, and I asked a translator to tell me what was that sign on it, and he said: US Imperialist Warmongers. He then realised what he'd said and we both had a good laugh. Security people were totally baffled by somebody like me wandering around with a security badge and they just couldn't understand it. I was quite often stopped.

One of the hardest times was when we wanted to stop by and see Associated Press and UPI up in Beijing, and of course, that was not planned – one foreigner talking to another, what on earth might they do? So at any rate, finally I was allowed in after a lot of talking to security people in the building along with my security people. Sort of, 'Oh, let the mad foreigner go,' I suppose. [It had been a case of] 'Stop by and have a beer if you're in Beijing, go and see Fred.' So I was in Beijing and much to the consternation of the security people I went and had a beer with Fred. From Vietnam days, of course. We used to look after the press quite a bit.

Howard Kleyn*'s experience with the cable-laying venture of the late 1960s – when there was a diplomatic freeze in relations – provides a keen example of China's business integrity and of how Hong Kong and China have altered over the passage of recent time.*

In the days when that cable was being mooted, and then laid, between Hong Kong and Kwangtung, it was agreed one day that we would meet our counterparts at the border, at a place called Shenzhen. We would actually join the cables together and get the thing going. We went along at 9 one morning; there was nothing but reeds, rice paddies, and a million mosquitoes, none of whom spoke English. We stood there thinking, 'It's 9 o'clock in the morning, lovely. I wonder if these chaps even exist.' Then suddenly down the hillside they came, the coolies with the cable over their shoulder. Yes, it was all agreed: the Chinese agreed to meet at that time, and they did.

Go back today and look at that same spot. You won't find it. Oh, the cable's still there, yes. But there's a city there. Not a village or a town, a city. Extraordinary, isn't it?

The spectacle of an electric storm over Hong Kong harbour

CHAPTER SEVEN

In extremity – Political and natural upheaval

Coups, earthquakes. I suppose I've got a warped sense of humour. I always manage to see the funny side.

John Howie

The new world in which Cable & Wireless was operating, with freshly independent nations and political turmoil, was also a world of far greater instability. Western companies, especially communications companies, were ready targets for dissidents. Thus many Company employees, and their families, found themselves in the midst of dangerous situations. Political upheaval, coups and revolutions, especially in Africa and South America, brought their fair share of life-threatening events – and black humour.

Chris Schofield *was among the last British people to be in Egypt, and experienced the unrest there before the revolution and the Suez crisis of the mid-1950s.*

We were in Alexandria from 1950 through to 1955 and had all the troubles. Well, not all. We got out before the Europeans were locked up or put under house arrest, but there was Faroukh's abdication, and Negeb coming into power, then Nasser taking over. In the Alex office there was a fair degree of nationalism amongst the operators, and they didn't like handling the traffic which we sent down to Suez for the soldiers who were stationed there. So every now and again we'd have a bit of a demonstration and a blow-up. In fact, at one time it got a bit nasty, threatening us because of being Europeans and being friends of the soldiers. Threatened physically. So we started doubling up on night duty. Instead of one of us being on night duty, one of us would be along in the engineer's office, so you felt you had a little bit of back-up there.

I remember one evening, I was on duty and one of the operators came in waving a revolver at me. It was really quite upsetting for a time because I thought the dangerous things of life had all gone by by then, but the supervisor was an Armenian and could talk anybody round to anything. He chatted up the bloke and eventually got the gun away from him. That particular operator I think was a bit mad, because he then got down on the floor and started chewing the chair leg.

Brian Pemberton *in East Africa some eight years later was to experience the first rumblings of armed antagonism to the rule of the post-independence leaderships. Cable & Wireless maintained an active commercial presence in many states that had formerly been British colonial territories, and were a reliable conduit for communications in an unstable political world.*

Nairobi was a large HF radio station ... I was there when the various mutinies occurred within the armies. Started in Kampala, up in Uganda. Although they kept a grip on it, just about, it was like tinder. Kampala barracks went one day, then in Tanganyika some soldiers broke out of barracks there; they didn't actually break out in Kenya. It was quite a tense time – and of course you're very busy, because there's a hell of a lot of press around who want to file stories and speak their pieces back to the BBC in London, and to America and so forth. It was quite tense for a while out there.

We were connecting traffic with [Presidents] Nyerere and Obote and Kenyatta. Their concerns were simple. Was it like lighting touchpaper in one place that would ignite in another barracks? ... They were quite nervous times and you knew more than most others because you had to sit in, keep a grip on the communications, making sure they could talk to each other.

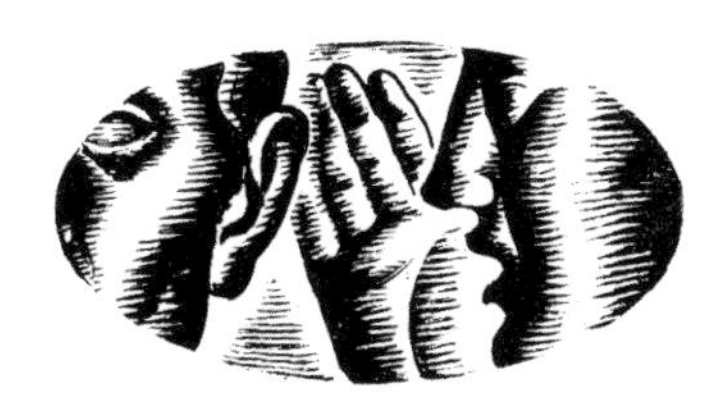

John Fuge *meanwhile was in West Africa, and in the midst of the first coup in the new nation of Sierra Leone.*

While I was there they had their coup, the first coup in Sierra Leone – and of course the first thing they do is seize the radio stations. We had a BBC reporter up at the radio station and we were doing voicecast back to the BBC on the deteriorating political situation. We heard up the land line from the town office that there'd been a coup, and so we got this guy packed off and out of there very quickly because they'd be after him. He actually drove out of the gate as the troops came in the gate. But they didn't go after him – they didn't know what to do so they came in and arrested all of us! That was really farcical.

We were high up on the hill overlooking Freetown Harbour, which is a huge natural harbour. It's an incredible place, and you have the iron ore ships coming in there and these are 75,000-ton ships, and we also controlled the shipping. We did the ship-to-shore from that radio station. We gave the ships their instructions: what buoy to tie up to, the pilot ... and all this stuff. All the details would be done from there. Well, when these guys came in we got a message out to London, before they came in, saying there was a coup taking place, the troops were now coming into the radio station and we're now going silent. Which we did. So we got the message out to the world, what was happening there. They put us all under arrest; they said, 'Don't do anything.' We said, 'Well, all this equipment is on.' And so they said, 'Well, you'd better switch it off.' So they took us down to the office. Where I was was high on the hill, and below were the old buildings where we had the transmitters and the diesel engines and so on. So we walked down to the transmitter hut and I went to press the button to switch it off, and the man said, 'No! Don't touch that.' I said, 'Well, I've got to switch it off.' He said, 'Well, don't touch that.' And I said, 'Well, I can't switch it off if I can't press this button.' So he thought about it, and he said, 'Then don't switch it off.' So we went back up the hill.

But the [harbour] radio: I guess about an hour passed, but the ship-to-shore radio was blasting. There were two or three very large ships coming into the harbour screaming for their instructions and staff were milling around, so the next thing was, 'Answer him.' So I picked up the microphone to answer him – 'Don't say anything. Don't transmit.' I said, 'Well, how can I answer him if I don't transmit?' It was absolutely incredible.

They had machine guns ... Well, the officer had a machine gun I didn't recognise, probably a Russian thing, and all the others had rifles with fixed bayonets on. So we were inclined to do what they said because they weren't, frankly, too bright. Anyway, in the end I said, 'Well, this is pretty serious. How can I get permission to tell those ships where to go and anchor before there is a huge accident in the harbour?' The officer had the gumption: he called headquarters, and I was told to come to coup headquarters. Did I have a car? Yes. So I took the troops. Two of the troops were told to take me down to headquarters. One of them kept his bayonet on and, anyway, we got down [to the car].

I had an Austin 1100 which I'd bought in England and shipped out to Freetown. It was a stupid car to take there but it was the pride of my life. The guy gets in the front, that's OK. But the guy who got in the back still had his bayonet on, and he put the rifle in first and it went straight through the roof of the car. 'Doesn't matter!' He put it on the floor and sat in. There was my car with a bayonet sticking out of the roof. And we drove up to coup headquarters. I eventually got to see, I'm not sure who, a bunch of officers and told them what was going on and basically they said, 'No. Go back to the station.' So the same thing happened on the way back, and then they left us there for a while with one person guarding us. That was stupid because basically what he did was, he took his bayonet off and put it down, his rifle was cocked and the safety catch off, he put his hands on top of the rifle and his head on the top and went to sleep. We were all joking about who was going to pull the trigger, because we could have all gone home. But we didn't.

I don't know how many hours passed. We did manage to get messages out to London when no one was listening, to say, 'Don't talk to us; but we're telling you we're all OK and so far no one's hurt.' That kind of thing. And eventually, it must have been four or five hours, the officers came, or an officer came back, and told us to all go home. So we went home. And things basically calmed down. The coup was successful, of course.

Then there was a curfew. I had curfew pass number thirteen, which didn't amuse me too much. When you went out it was incredible. To go out: you'd get called, you'd got to go up to the radio station and it's after curfew hours so you had to go and get in your car and you weren't allowed to call anybody, you just had to go – Go. And the minute you started going you headed on to the main road and the next thing you knew there was a three-ton lorry bearing down on you, and a platoon of troops with all their machine guns pointing at you saying, 'Who are you and where are you going?' You'd say, 'I'm Cable & Wireless and I've got to go to work.' 'Ah – Cable & Wireless. Very good. Follow us.' Now you had an armed guard and they were going to try to persuade you how good they were at guarding you, and that was probably worse than anything else you could have. But anyway, there were no incidents.

There was a lot of killing, but we didn't see any. The British had an Italian ship standing off Sierra Leone: if they had to evacuate people we were all supposed to go down to it. This was ridiculous when you think about it. We had to go right back into the main town and assemble at the jetty where they would take us out – and the place where they were asking us to assemble was where most of the killing was done. So it was not too clever a plan, but never mind. It was just lucky it didn't happen. We had a sail boat, a small GP14, which we had laden with dried milk and tins of stuff. If it got bad we were determined we were going to go to sea and sail down, anywhere, sail to the next country. We didn't do that either, but we were ready to do it.

It was one of the most terrifying times, that's right. You do what you can. It's extremely scary, especially when you know somebody's pointing a gun at you and he's not too educated as it were and he might do anything.

It settled down, but it wasn't very pleasant. We were on the last ship to leave Sierra Leone. But when the ship pulled away from the dock and the tugs had dropped their lines, I hasten to add that the loudspeakers played *Rule Britannia* and we sailed out of the harbour.

Oh, the bayonet hole was fixed. I claimed on the Company on that and it raised a lot of eyebrows: 'What *is* this man talking about? A *bayonet* through the top of his car?'

John Nash *experienced the same coup, but he had rather less alarming experiences.*

While I was in Freetown there was a coup. We were quietly doing our thing in the [town] office when suddenly an army lorry screeched to a halt outside and all these soldiers jumped out with rifles. They made us all line up against the wall and switch everything off, which was a bit unnerving.

About ten minutes later an officer walked in and handed out the ammunition, so we needn't have worried.

They gradually calmed down and eventually we were allowed to switch on again and carry on.

John Howie *has lived through many of the coups and revolutions that have rocked the nations of South America, especially those in Argentina and Bolivia (where he still lives). His ironic detachment shines through.*

The abortive coup in Argentina, which was the nasty one, was in 1954 when they were bombarding the Plaza and killing everyone, and then the mob broke loose, and burned the churches. That was a bit hair-raising, I must admit, because all law and order disappeared. But we put down steel shutters in the street, and another engineer who had come in and I – we were the two expats, the first floor was the managerial section, and the instrument room was on the second floor – we were up there peering out of the window. Actually, I went up on the roof to watch the Gloucester Meteors that were flying around but the Peronistas who were on the opposite corner (but later got wiped out) started taking pot-shots. I decided perhaps it wasn't a very good thing to be seen on the roof so I went downstairs again, and we watched out of the window the mobs all streaming around.

Our office would have been about four blocks from Plaza de Mayo, towards Corrientes. We watched the mob streaming past, and one of the messengers came in, saying he was very sorry he had been so long delivering a message but he had been ordered by the Peronistas to join the march. He said he had had to go along in the march until he could escape and pop up a side street somewhere, and he was very sorry. We heard the bombs going off, and the windows were rattling, and the planes were screaming around, but in the building itself there wasn't very much going on.

The successful revolution in 1955, when they blasted away the Peronistas, was a bit ... Well, it wasn't *really* hairy, because we were under army protection. They came in and said, 'Can we put down the steel shutters?', and the captain said, 'Look, I'm going to put a machine-gun in your doorway' – we had a sort of recessed entry – and I said 'Yes, OK, fine,' and went back upstairs. I was on watch. We looked out of the window and the tanks were lined up. We could see the tanks. We were one block from the main avenue and the tanks were on the avenue. And we heard afterwards they had sent a guy in with a white flag and a surrender demand, and they had shot him and thrown him out of the window. To which the army didn't take very kindly. So they opened fire at point blank range, and using explosives and incendiaries just blew the place apart.

The other revolutions didn't really interfere with the ordinary way of life. I was driving down from Mendoza – I used to drive through the night if I had to go down to Buenos Aires because I preferred driving then, you could see the lights of a vehicle in the distance. A torch was waving across the road and I pulled in. As I came in I realised there were tanks on both sides of the road. I pulled up and an officer came over, sort of saluted, and he said, 'Good morning.' I said, 'Good morning, what's going on?' He said, 'Didn't you know there's a revolution going on?' I said, 'No'. He said, 'Where have you come from?' I said, 'I've come from Mendoza', which was about three hours away. He said, 'Weren't you listening to the radio?' I said, 'Yes, I was listening to a Paraguayan station, I like the guitar.' 'Well,' he said, 'there's a revolution. Where are you going?' 'I'm going to Buenos Aires, what are you going to do about that?' 'Look, you'll meet the other lot about three kilometres down the road. They might let you go through and they might not. But as far as I'm concerned you can carry on.' Fine, and on down the road, another torch waving across. The guy demanded, 'Where the hell have you come

The Western Telegraph Company offices in Buenos Aires

from?' I said, 'Mendoza.' 'How did you get through?' I said, 'They were very nice, they let me come through.' 'How many tanks have they got?' 'I couldn't tell but there seemed to be a lot. They're on both sides of the road.' 'Oh, all right, carry on.' It was all very polite. Once I'd got past the second line of troops there was no further problem. Got into Buenos Aires, everything was normal ...

It was the same in La Paz. When we had Natusz Busch's revolution in 1979, everybody was talking about it on the cocktail circuit. We had the Organization of American States meeting here, and they were all up in town in the Sheraton Hotel. The Company was operating [in La Paz still]. As I say, on the cocktail circuit everybody was saying, 'Yes, there's going to be a revolution.' 'Oh, when?' 'When the OAS conference finishes ...'

I didn't bother about it. Maybe I've got a problem. I drove up to town on 1 November. The Company had a car park behind the police station at the time. I just left the car, the Land Rover I had then, and walked up. A car screamed to a halt, a chap stuck his hand out. 'John, go home! There's a revolution!' 'Oh,' I said, 'I've got to be in the office, obviously.' I walked on. Everybody was going thataway, and I was walking thisaway. I ducked down, I crossed the main street, and there were some tanks further up the hill. I turned into our road and walked up, and there was a tank there. The man looked at me, and I looked at him, and he said 'Buenos dias,' and I said 'Buenos dias, señor,' and I walked down, walked into the office, no problem.

We had a lot of work to do.

I had had a letter from a friend in South Africa saying some South Africans were coming here and could I look them up and extend courtesies – the old ETC style. Lo and behold, they turned up the day of the revolution. So I called them up, said 'I'll pick you up this evening, 7 o'clock,' and they said, 'Do you mind if we bring a friend and his wife we'd met up with, an American coastguard captain?' 'No,' I said, 'I don't mind at all.' They'd also invited the South African ambassador, and I'd told him we'd meet outside the Sucre Palace Hotel ... I drove up and everybody was streaming down the street trying to get out of town. No way was I going to get up there ... First, I picked up the American coastguard commander and his wife. The manager of the Sheraton refused to let them come out, and the coastguard commander said, 'Look, I've been invited to this gentleman's house, in Calacota.' Eventually the manager said, 'All right, but on your own head be it.' So I said we're going straight down to Calacota. 'That's right,' he said, 'go straight down to Calacota.' So of course we went straight uptown. We met this mob streaming down from the top part of the city. I parked the car, and said to the American, 'Do you know how to drive one of these things?' He said, 'Sure.' I said, 'Stay here and if you see people actually start running, and you hear shots, get the hell out of here, go straight up this road here, turn left, take the one on the right, carry on to the end, and you'll come to my house.'

I walked up the road, pushing my way through the crowd to the Sucre Palace Hotel. They had their steel doors closed, just a fraction open. Luckily being thin I sneaked in through the door, walked over to the counter, and I said, 'Is Mr – he had an Afrikaaner name – here?' The girl went all of a judder, and she started looking through the register. The chap was standing there: 'Are you looking for me?' I said, 'Yes, come on, let's get the hell out.' We pushed our way out, and just at that minute the South African ambassador arrived in his car. Horn blaring and everything. He pulled up outside, so we leapt in his car, we drove down the road and picked up the Land Rover.

We went home. We had dinner. The house had on the first floor a sort of glassed-in verandah, and we sat there and watched the gunships up on the Alto – where the airport is ... Apparently the *campesinos* and the trade unionists and everybody had risen up in arms, and they were trying to take the airport. Somebody told them the Cubans were standing by, had planes all ready to land. So they had these gunships, and we sat there watching these damn things. And the coastguard commander said, 'We'd better get back to the hotel.' It was something like 11 o'clock. Just at that moment somebody out in the street opened up with a machinegun – just outside the house. He hurriedly changed his mind. I said, 'You can sleep on the floor, on spare beds,' and we got everybody bedded down for the night.

The next morning I took them back but everything was paralysed. So I said,

'Would you like to look around down here?' I showed them around Calacota, which was all normal. And the coastguard commander was amazed: 'Look, there's people lying on the grass in the sunshine, in their bathing suits, and up there they're shooting each other.' 'Well,' I said, 'that's the way it goes here, son.'

Here [in La Paz], we've had one – two – three – four revolutions. But only one really bad one. When Garcia Mesa took over, in 1981. The office called me up: would I go down to the counter? So I went down, and there was a man in a long trenchcoat with two goons alongside. I said, 'Hello, good morning', and he said, 'You've got to close the office down.' So I said, 'You can't! Who are you anyway?' 'Oh, I'm from the ...' He produced his warrant, that he was from the G3 in the Army. And his two goons showed me their revolvers, and the various other pieces of kit they were carrying. So I said, 'Why?' 'Because,' he said, 'you are carrying a lot of lies. Disseminating lies all over the world.' I said, 'All we are, we're like a railway train. Somebody comes along and puts a parcel on the train, the train takes it up the other end – and if it's a bomb at the other end it's not the railway's fault.' 'No, no, no.' He wouldn't listen. 'You can't close us down – we have every embassy in La Paz connected to our exchange, and you're going to cut all them off. Apart from that, it's against international law.' I wasn't sure whether it was or not, but I'm sure he didn't know and I thought, 'Hell, it's a good chance.' He hesitated for a while, then said 'No.' He pulled an Uzi out from under his trenchcoat. He pointed it at me. 'You've got to close.'

I called up from the office downstairs, and said, 'Shut down all the circuits.' I said to him, 'I want to see somebody about this – you can't just come in and do that!' He just shrugged his shoulders, turned around and walked off. I followed him out, and I said to the staff, 'I'm going to sort this one out.' So I walked round to the Plaza Murilla, which is where the government offices are – there's the Congress on one side and the Presidential Palace on the other, with a lot of tatty shops on the other two sides, and a big plaza in the middle, where they hanged one of the presidents on a lamp post, back in 1946. The lamp post is now a public monument.

Anyway, I walked up there, and I turned the corner. There was a soldier there with a wretched bazooka or something, who said 'Halt!' I looked past him, and the whole plaza was jammed with tanks and armoured cars. I said, 'I want to see whoever's in charge of communications.' He called the sergeant, and the sergeant came out. A bit more polite, a bit more educated. I explained to him, 'I'm the Manager of Cable West Coast, I want to see the man in charge of communications round here.' He said, 'You can't come into the plaza, do you mind staying here?'

Eventually a colonel showed up, we had all the typical how's your father that you have to go through in this country, then he said, 'What's your problem?' 'Your guys have just come round and closed down my office. I've got all the embassies in La Paz screaming blue murder because they can't report.' He said, 'You know what the problem is. The news that is getting out to Europe and the United States is all against General Garcia Mesa.' 'OK, but that's not my fault! You know what they're doing – it's nothing to do with me and my telex, they've cut off all telephones outbound, and never thought to cut off the inbound ones! It's quite simple, what's happening is these characters in London for the past ten hours or so have been calling up their correspondents here, who have had their tape recorders, have dictated everything, and are sending it out over the telephone line on an incoming call. They set their machine on – *zip* – it's all in London or New York or wherever – it's nothing to do with me.' 'Mmm.' It hadn't occurred to him. 'You've missed the boat there, mate.'

He said, 'I'll give you permission to open again, but you've got to censor all the traffic.' 'What, me? I can't do that – there's stacks of the stuff.' 'Tell your staff that they've got to censor the messages before they send them. We will hold you responsible for any information that gets out.' 'Fine,' I said, 'OK, fair enough.' I went back, and told the counter staff, 'Look at the messages and make sure they don't say anything nasty about General Garcia Mesa, then send them on.' Before I left this chap, I had said, 'It's not fair to ask me or my staff to censor. You send down some military censors.' 'Yes,' he said, 'I'll do that. In the meantime while you're waiting for them you can open up. I'll send some military censors. Ciao, OK.' They never showed up – we just carried on.

I suppose I've got a warped sense of humour. I always manage to see the funny side of it all.

John Slaughter *in his role as roving finder of business was also at times a roving finder of trouble.*

We went into Uganda, for the first time ... It was the year Idi Amin went, 1977 or 1978. They'd had problems with their accounts and they might be looking for a friend to help. We actually flew into Entebbe when they were still fighting Idi Amin just to the north of Kampala. We had to fly in under the visible range of people keeping an eye on the airport ... So we met and arranged with this chap we found who had a twin-engined Italian aeroplane and was willing to fly in. Very few people were willing to fly in. They were still shooting at aeroplanes that tried to land in Entebbe. He said when we got there – he kept very low – 'I have to go round and approach the runway at the last moment, so don't get worried if it looks like the wing's going to scrape on the ground.' So he went very low and swooped in, and he said, 'They can't get the guns down this far.' Anyway, we sort of wandered around, parked the aeroplane. Nobody challenged us. Some people who looked a bit official came towards us at one stage, and asked if we had any newspapers. People were interested in looking for outside newspapers to see what was going on in their country.

When we got out of the airport we found a chap from the Uganda P&T who had come down to meet us, because we had to let them know we were coming. On the way from Entebbe to Kampala we went through fourteen road checks, military, all run by the Tanzanian army, the average age of which seemed to be about 14, all with rifles, and all wanting cigarettes. Two or three of them, rifle up your nostril asking if you had any cigarettes. It was a bit worrying. They only wanted one or two each, not boxes – they just wanted to have a smoke, they were all young lads. Eventually we got in to Kampala. Politically the whole place was in turmoil.

Given the nature of the locations in which Cable & Wireless is and has been based, the incidence of natural calamity has been high. Most people who served the Company overseas will have experienced at some point in their careers hurricanes, tornadoes and typhoons, earthquakes and volcanic eruptions, raging fires and freezing temperatures.

Jubilation and fear as Tanzania's troops invaded Uganda to oust Idi Amin – with Cable & Wireless still selling telecommunications in the thick of it

Ted Amor *was based in Fayal, in the Azores, as Branch Engineer in the late 1950s, when its volcanic origins made its presence felt.*

The place [Fayal, Azores] was going on beautifully well, and then one morning, about 9 o'clock in the morning, the lighthouse keeper on the other side of the island at Capello, noticed a stain in the water about two or three hundred yards offshore. And there was a slight rumble in the ground. He rang up the town: they knew what was coming, and it did. The volcano started, about five hundred yards offshore.

It started off with smoke coming out of the sea and then ash, and then the island started forming ... It was something to do: we all got our cars, we went out to see how the volcano was getting on. We all took photographs, had picnics there, went back. It got bigger and bigger and bigger. Then the tremblings were worse – they were having hell down in the office. The poor old watchkeepers, with all the delicate instruments. Then the dust started spreading all over the island: it was magnetic, you could pick it up like iron filings with a magnet because it had an iron base. And of course there were relays going faulty because of the intense magnetic field. It was driving the watchkeepers mad. Got bigger and bigger and bigger. Then it did literally, after about three or four months of expanding, blow its top.

There was a huge explosion, great chunks of rock in the air and the island trembled, three or four houses fell down. Nobody was hurt because the government had evacuated the area. And at that particular time my daughter was born. With the whole island rocking.

Anyway, the newspapers got hold of it. Apart from the damn nuisance of it, we were having fun. We were going up to see how it was getting on, even after the big explosion. I got a telegram from my father, who didn't flap, and it said 'Seriously disturbed' – I'd sent him a telegram telling him that he was a grandfather – 'Please advise if Maureen and Sue have been evacuated.' So I said, 'What the hell's all this about?' I'd written to him and sent him photographs. The *Daily Express* had sent a reporter, one Victor Brittenden ... He couldn't get to Fayal because there was only a weekly boat service to the main airport of the islands, which was Santa Maria, a hundred miles away. He parked himself in the bar of the Terra Nostra Hotel, and wrote his copy from there, sent it back by air.

The *Express* headline: 'Death Strikes Terror Island, Thousands Flee.' There was no fleeing, no deaths, nothing. Well, we were all having a ball, it was great fun, you see.

Paul Foster *had left Cable & Wireless in Barbados in 1951 to become a journalist, but he maintained his old links. In September 1955 when Hurricane Janet devastated the island his contacts paid off.*

We knew Hurricane Janet was coming. I got my wife and whatever number of children it was at the time, and sent them up into the country with her sister who lived in a plantation house, a nice strong house. So I knew she was OK. Then I went down to the newspaper and we did try to get it out, but we lost power at 11 o'clock. And the hurricane raged until 3 or 4. So I decided to go to the cable station, my old hunting ground, and send out a message about it. It was really quite an experience in a car to try and get from Bridgetown to the cable station at St Lawrence. I had to make so many diversions. Trees across the road. It was a mess. I finally got to the cable station and – using a *bit* of journalistic licence, I suppose – said, 'Not one square mile of this little island has been spared the ravages of Hurricane Janet.' I got this big story. We used to subscribe to a service that any time the word Barbados was used, they'd send it back to us at the *Advocate.* This stuff started to come back: what it did, it galvanised the outside world into sending us help, all sorts of foodstuff. I was the first person to get the news out, I knew it was my story, and it helped to get us back on our feet again.

John Howie *seemed to have enjoyed more than his fair share of natural and man-made calamity. Not only did he find himself caught in many a South American revolution, but he also encountered hurricanes and earthquakes.*

In Jamaica, hurricanes were a problem. We collected the weather reports from the other islands and passed them on to Miami, and made a big plastic-covered map for the office where we could plot the hurricanes ourselves. In 1952 one headed straight for us. We battened down the house, filled the bath with water, checked torches and so on, and then watched it coming. The evening sky turned an evil purple, and then came a sound like an Underground train approaching. But a really big one. I put the family under the bed, which had an iron frame, and prowled around checking windows. I peered through the boarded-up windows, and was horrified to see sheets of corrugated iron flying round like paper. Eventually the eye of the storm arrived, and all was quiet until it passed and the fury resumed. Towards dawn the rains came, but the house was still sound.

My wife then decided she was going to have her baby (our second). So a mad rush to get the car out – and I found a palm tree down, right across the drive and resting on the roof of the house. I had never heard it. Some hearty hacking with a machete and I got mobile, and we raced down the flooded streets to the hospital. Where the nurses were sweeping the water out of the front door. They had lost their roof.

Then down to the office. Wreckage everywhere. A cruise liner had its bows in a hotel swimming pool, the phones were all out, and the office was partially flooded from a hole in the roof. One or two cables were still working: it was amusing to watch a fork bias corrector clicking away in a pool of water, the glass case having been broken.

We worked like mad all day, clearing the water, fixing what we could and getting back into shape ... Luckily we had a cable ship in the harbour and she was the only ship afloat that morning. She had put down two buoys on the bow anchors and steamed full ahead all night steering on the buoys. The skipper later said their anemometer was reading 175 mph when it blew away. We had a police radio car in the car park so we could relay any important messages to Government; later in the day I asked the sergeant if he could contact any car near the hospital and see how my wife was. He soon came back, and told me I had a son ...

Clearing a pass in the Andes after a blizzard in 1953

As Manager of the Line, the overland telegraph between Argentina and Peru, in the 1960s, John Howie also had the physical barrier and the geological instability of the Andes to cope with.

To cross the Andes, in the summer I could either drive through the railway tunnel, bumping along over the sleepers, or climb up over the top where the Cristo [statue] marked the frontier at about 5000-odd metres. (Our underground cables went across higher than the Cristo.) I preferred the top route, as the views were fantastic and I was always worried about earthquakes in the tunnel.

When a really big earthquake hit, I got an emergency call from the Chilean inspector asking for wire, insulators and the like. So I loaded the station wagon up to the limit (we had a truck, but that was rather too big to get through the tunnel), and arriving at the tunnel I found no one there so I decided to go through. Hoping a train would not be coming the other way. I needn't have worried, as the railway on the Chilean side was hanging in ribbons. It took them three months to repair. The Chilean police were so surprised to see me driving out of the tunnel, and they said I would never get down as the road was blocked by a landslide. I went down slowly, as the ground was still shaking, and came to the blockage. Luckily, the foreman recognised me and told his men to lift the car onto the railway, which was undamaged at this point, so I drove along the railway for a few miles until I came to a crossing and got back onto the road. Then down into Los Andes, the repeater station. The Chilean police could not believe I had driven across from Argentina.

I don't mind hurricanes too much as one can watch them and prepare. But earthquakes are nasty, they catch you unawares. Driving the Chilean truck through the hills one day, I suddenly saw a biggish crack appear between the front wheels and race ahead up the road. The odd lurching beforehand I had assumed was the dirt road.

Typhoons, floods, earthquakes, volcanoes – all part of the expatriate life.

CHAPTER EIGHT

Over the horizon

When one of the men whose stories are included in this book first approached Cable & Wireless wanting to work for them, he recalled that the initial appeal the Company had for him was that he might get out and see the world. 'But not entirely that. In the process of the interview, I was taken up to see the instrument room. And I thought it was the closest thing to magic I had ever seen.'[1]

For Ron Werngren, that magic never disappeared, he says – no matter where the Company sent him or what the new technology was. He was not alone in his reactions. Those twin themes, of where people were sent and what technology new or old they were asked to install, maintain and administer, have been uppermost throughout the testimonies and anecdotes that have been gathered together here.

The official history of Cable & Wireless, published on the occasion of the modern Company's golden jubilee in 1979, was called *Girdle Round the Earth.* The title for this book, *Voices Over the Horizon,* similarly evokes the Company's global character. It is also intended to give the sense of passage. On the one hand, there was the passage of people. They moved away from Britain for a considerable portion of their lives, working to serve the Company, and they even called themselves The Exiles, yet however far away they were still felt themselves to be just over the horizon. And on the other hand, there is the passing of time.

The Cable & Wireless of today bears many resemblances to the Cable & Wireless of the past – the wide spread of places served, the provision of telecommunications systems for countries around the world, and its British roots. Many of the people who work for Cable & Wireless today spend a considerable amount of time travelling and working away from their native environment. Yet the expatriate lifestyle that was once the hallmark of the Company has been eclipsed, and it disappeared during the passing of the memories that have been tapped for this book.

For all its global reach, Cable & Wireless was always a relatively small operation. The numbers it employed throughout the world in the 1970s, on the eve of privatisation, were some 10,500, a figure barely larger than the staff of 9,500 the Company had in the late 1920s. In that context, the places of which you might ask 'Can you imagine thirty English people entertaining thirty English people?' or where 'at Christmas you'd attend a round of parties where you'd see the same twelve people ... And what we talked about I really can't remember' make more sense.[2] Numbers did rise considerably after the 1970s, a decade in which Cable & Wireless had been in considerable flux. By 1980 there were nearly 12,000 people, and in 1990 the workforce was approaching 38,000. It may have been well on the way to becoming a major telecommunications player, but Cable & Wireless never quite lost the close, familial feel that many have identified as one of its particular characteristics.

People who worked for Cable & Wireless share a sense of pride in what they achieved, and the nature of the overseas life that many of them followed reinforced their sense of 'otherness'. That was partly because of being expatriate, and partly because of the fact that most people at home were barely (if at all) aware of the existence of the Company for which they worked. Time and again, people have described the old telegraph cables as being 'almost like a religion'. There is a keen sense of a shared companionship in sometimes hostile environments, or in the more remote places of people being thrown onto their own devices. Making do and mending, or entertaining themselves.

There is inevitably a keen sense of nostalgia throughout many of the first-hand accounts in this book. Many contrast the cocoon of the old Company way of life with a faster, short-term, short-contract, modern way of working. Although they regret the change, most recognise its inevitability – and they can point to the extent to which things they experienced had changed from a previous generation – and appreciate that there was a shift in British society and the world economy that dictated change. Cable & Wireless is a global enterprise, and its vision was global from the start. Although people did not necessarily realise it at the time, perhaps the most decisive break with the past came not with technology but with the political and commercial changes that produced privatisation. And that, as they say, is another story.

[1] See above, p. 26.

[2] Ted Amor, above, p. 57; John Davenport, above, p. 81.

GLOSSARY

This selection of short definitions for some of the technical and specific terms that appear in the course of the book is designed as an aid to those readers who are not familiar with the technologies of telecommunication or the corporate workings of Cable & Wireless

A/E, Assistant Engineer. First level of promotion for most of the *F1* staff above the level of *watchkeeper* after their training and first posting.

Advanced Course. Tuition at the Company's training college after a few years in the field, necessary for further promotion.

AT&T. Principal American telecommunications company.

automatic transmission. Sending of messages using a pre-punched paper tape, in place of direct manual keying.

balance. Equilibrium on a *duplex cable* providing the ability to have messages pass in both directions. Maintaining and rectifying the balance was an essential part of a cable technician's work.

branch, station. Company term for one of its *cable* or *radio* offices, usually overseas.

Branch Engineer. More senior member of the staff on a *branch*, with overall responsibility for engineering and for maintaining and renewing the mechanical equipment.

cable. General term for a covered wire or strand of wires, often laid underwater, for transmission of *telegraph* messages and, later, voice *telephone* calls. By extension, a *telegram* was often called a cable.

cable chain. Linked run of submarine *cables*, forming connection over a great distance.

cable code. Modification of *Morse Code*, using positive and negative electrical impulses in place of the short and long dots and dashes.

cablese. Short forms of words and phrases for economy in sending *telegram* messages.

cable ship. Dedicated vessel used for laying and repair of submarine *cables*.

coaxial. Multi-stranded *cable*, capable of carrying far greater volumes of *traffic* including speech, introduced in the 1960s.

COMPAC. Pacific section of the round-the-world *coaxial cable* laid in the 1960s through Commonwealth initiative, between Canada and New Zealand and Australia via Fiji.

consolidation. Six months initial experience in a *cable* or *wireless* office after college tuition.

Court of Directors. Company usage until the 1990s for its Board of Directors.

duplex. Transmission along a *cable* allowing messages to be both sent and received at the same time.

earth station. Term for the ground installation used in *satellite* communications, particularly incorporating a large reflecting dish.

ETC, Eastern. Eastern Telegraph Company, formed in 1872 from the merger of a number of Sir John Pender's *telegraph* companies.

F1. Company term for its elite expatriate workforce, that until the 1970s filled all the senior positions at a *branch.*

five-unit. Adaptation of *cable code,* adopted in the 1950s, to improve the volume and speed of traffic on the submarine *telegraph cables.*

General Examination. Examination taken by *F1* staff after their initial period of employment that allowed them to move up through the Company's grade system.

General Manager. Usually the senior person at a branch, and the position to which most *F1* staff aspired.

Head Office. Company term for its London-based central organisation, that operated considerably close control over the activities of the *branches.*

HF. High Frequency *radio* transmission, later superseded by *VHF* and *UHF.*

instrument room. Principal room in a *cable station* containing the electromechanical equipment for sending and receiving messages.

key, Morse key. Electromechanical device for direct sending of messages in *Morse Code* or *cable code.*

land line. Term for *cable* carried over land rather than underwater. The most important of the Company's land lines was that which crossed the Andes linking Argentina and Chile.

local staff. Non-expatriate staff at a *branch,* locally recruited.

local repair. Minor repair of a submarine *cable* undertaken by the engineers at a *branch.* Larger or deeper water repairs were undertaken by a *cable ship.*

Marconi. Company founded by Guglielmo Marconi (1874–1937) in 1897 for *radio* communication, that amalgated with the Eastern and Associated Telegraph Companies in 1929 to form the company that became Cable & Wireless.

mess. Company name for communal accommodation, especially at larger *branches,* for bachelors.

microwave. Communication using a wave in the radiation spectrum between normal *radio* waves and infra-red.

mirror galvanometer. Early optical device for receiving *telegraph* messages.

Morse Code. Combinations of dots and dashes, short and long pulses, devised by Samuel Morse (1791–1872) to represent the letters of the alphabet.

operating, operator. Company term for the process and personnel preparing for transmission and receiving the *telegraph* messages. Although originally applied to the *cable* system, by extension it was later applied to those working in the *radio* system.

optical fibre. *Cable* made of glass, introduced in the 1980s, capable of carrying considerable volumes of voice, television and other *traffic*. *Traffic* is transmitted along the glass fibre in the form of flashes or pulses of infra-red light.

P&T, PTT. General telecommunications term for a national entity concerned with Posts and Telegraphs, subsequently Posts, Telegraphs and Telephones.

perforator, hand perforator. Device that, automatically or manually, punches the holes in the *slip* used for transmission of *telegraph* messages.

Porthcurno, PK. Cornish coastal location (PK being the Company abbreviation), where the submarine *cables* came ashore.

radio. *Telegraphy* or *telephony* without wires, using radio waves. Advances in radio communication have used ever-higher frequencies: *Marconi's* original experiments used long wave, and subsequently a short-wave 'beam' system, to be superseded by *HF*, *VHF*, *UHF* and ultimately *satellite* systems.

radio receiving station. Installation with aerials for receiving *radio* communications.

radio transmitting station. Separate installation with aerials for transmitting *radio* communications.

regen, regenerator. Technical advance of the 1920s, increasing the volume and speed of *traffic* by allowing automatic reshaping and retiming of signals at intermediate relay stations along the length of a *cable*.

SANGCOM. Important series of contracts since the 1970s to provide *HF radio* communications systems for the Saudi Arabian National Guard.

satellite. Form of communication using orbiting or geo-stationary man-made objects above the earth's atmosphere, reflecting super-high frequency *radio* waves to and from the earth's surface.

SEACOM. South-East Asia section of the round-the-world *coaxial cable* laid in the 1960s through Commonwealth initiative, linking Hong Kong, Singapore and Sabah with Australia.

service call, service message. Company term for business or personal communication via the *cable* or *wireless* links.

ship watch. Special *watch* using ship-to-shore communication with a cable *station*, particularly in locating a break in a submarine *cable*.

shore end. End of a submarine *cable* where it comes ashore, and is linked to the *cable station*.

slip. Paper tape used for sending or receiving *cable* messages.

station. See *branch.*

telegram. Written message sent by *telegraph.*

telegraph, telegraphy. Electric signalling system for sending messages over distance invented by Charles Wheatstone and William Fothergill Cooke in 1837.

telephone, telephony. Instrument or system for reproducing sound at a distance, by electrical means, using *cable, satellite* or *radio* transmission.

telex. Communication using teleprinter exchange, *telegraph* transmission to and from a typewriter-type keyoard.

The Tunnels. Underground workings at *Porthcurno* to house the British end of the international cable connections, originally built for security in the Second World War.

TORS. Teleprinter on Radio. *Radio*-based *telex* communication.

tour. Company term for the length of time, often four years, spent working at one or more *branches* before taking lengthy leave.

traffic. Messages sent on the *telegraph* or *telephone* system.

tropo, tropospheric scatter. Form of *radio*-based transmission using special aerials, bouncing off the troposphere, the lowest layer of the atmosphere.

UHF. Ultra High Frequency *radio* transmission.

VHF. Very High Frequency *radio* transmission.

watch, watchkeeper. Shifts (usually six hours) during which younger technicians during or soon after their *consolidation* supervised the running of the *telegraph* system at a *station.*

wireless. General term for *radio.*

WTC, Western. Western Telegraph Company. Principal Cable & Wireless operating company in South America, formed from existing companies in 1899.

INTERVIEW MATERIAL

Interviews and conversations for this and the book that will follow have been conducted to date with: Ted & Maureen Amor, Norman Ampleford, Pamela Aylmore, Jim Bairstow, Maurice & Mary Bane, A. 'Herbie' Blundell, Patricia Bosdet, John Bragg, Chris Brain, Paul Carrington, Gustavo Coll, Ian Corrall, Pat Cowan, Peter & Grace Critchley, Dominic Crolla, John Davenport, Barbara Ducat-Amos, Tony & Marie-Louise Dunne, Arthur Farmer, Paul Foster, John Fuge, Fung Hak Ming, E. 'Sonny' Gilkes, Wally Hardiman, Richard & Brenda Histed, Y.C. Ho, John Howie, Howard Kleyn, Basil Leighton, Albert Lorens, Janet March-Penney, Helen Marsden, Derek & Elizabeth Moore, Peter Moulson, John Nash, Rod Olsen, John Packer, Brian Pemberton, Alan Petts, Ken Reece, Jimmy & Bernice Richards, John Rippengal, Chris Schofield, Richard Selby, Colin Sharp, Sidney & Joan Sherwood, John Slaughter, Noel Hare Smith, Jonathan Solomon, Jeanne Spooner, Colin & Patricia Stubbs, Wendy Suart, Pat Sykes, John Tibbles, Keith & Pat Warren, George Warwick, Ron Werngren, Pete Wolfe, Brian Woods and John Worrall.

Jeanne Spooner and Amanda Howard transcribed many of the resulting tapes. The tape of the interview with the late Brian Suart was lent by Wendy Suart. Personal memoirs and transcripts of other interviews conducted at earlier dates were consulted in the Cable & Wireless archives.

BIBLIOGRAPHY

Charles Allen, *Plain tales from the Raj* (1975)

Charles Allen, *Tales from the Dark Continent* (1979)

Charles Allen, *Tales from the South China Seas* (1983)

J.P. Bairstow, *East of Colombo 1945–1949* (1995)

Hugh Barty-King, *Girdle round the earth. The story of Cable & Wireless* (1979)

Arthur C. Clarke, *Voice across the sea*, 2nd edition (1974)

Austin Coates, *Quick tidings of Hong Kong* (1990)

Cathy Courtney & Paul Thompson, *City Lives. The changing voices of British finance* (1996)

Alexander Frater, *Beyond the blue horizon: on the track of Imperial Airways* (1986)

Charles Graves, *The thin red lines* (1946)

Duff Hart-Davis, *Ascension. The story of a South Atlantic island* (1972)

Duff Hart-Davis, *The gold of St Matthew* (1970)

Peter Pagnamenta & Richard Overy, *All our working lives* (1984)

Harry Ritchie, *The last pink bits. Travels through the remnants of the British Empire* (1997)

Bernard Stonehouse, *Wideawake Island* (1960)

J.F. Stray, *Inside an international. Forty years in Cable & Wireless* (1982)

Wendy Suart, *The lingering eye. Recollections of North Borneo* (1993)

Paul Thompson, *The voice of the past: oral history* (1978)

Simon Winchester, *Outposts. Journeys to the surviving relics of the British Empire* (1985)

Zodiac

CAWPA News

INDEX

Page numbers in **bold** *refer to illustrations*
Local place names are listed under individual countries.

Aden 56, 61, 62, 78, 92, **93**, 94, 96, 106, 161; *see also* Yemen
Africa 169, 171, 181, 189, 197, 246; *see also individual countries*
African Direct Telegraph 171
air conditioning 48, 49, 55, 66
airport, airstrip 120, 221, 258
alcohol *see* drink
Algeria
  Algiers 148
Allen, Charles xxi
Amazon, River 46
Amin, Idi 258, **259**
Amor, Maureen 79–80, **109**
Amor, Ted 14–15, 39–40, **41**, 56–7, 66, 69, 96, 159–60, 165, 239–40, 260–1
analogue 168, 235
Andes **263**, 264
Anne, Princess 236
Arabian Gulf 47, 53, 56, 86, 110, 203, 205; *see also individual countries*
Argentina 179, 181, 251, 264
  Buenos Aires 21, 26, 69, 110, 181, 251, 252, **253**, 254
  Mendoza 252, 254
armed forces 29, 34, 246-7; *see also* war
  Army 132, 143, 258
  Fleet Air Arm 144
  Royal Air Force 132, 136
  Royal Marines 134
  Royal Naval Volunteer Reserve 132
  Royal Navy 120, 132
Ascension Historical (now Heritage) Society 119, 120
Ascension Island 4, 64, **65**, 89, 98, 113–23, **116**, 136, 165, **188**
  Georgetown 119, **121**
  Green Mountain 115, 117, 118, 119, 123
  Magistrate, Justice of the Peace 98, 114, 199
  toilets 117, 123
Asiadata 212
astronomy 122
  eclipse of the moon 154
AT&T 119, 150, 152, 168, 214
Australia 12, 30, 40, 66, 88, 99, 114, 115, 133, 152, 213, 217, 237
  Perth, Western Australia 49, 114, 126
  Sydney 30, 49
Aylmore, Pamela 11–12, 211–12
Aziz al Ayar, General Abdul 198
Azores 56, 80, 260
  Fayal 79, 80, 260
  Santa Maria 260

bachelors 39, 43, 50, 55, 69, 119, 123, 152, 173; *see also* marriage; mess
Bahrain 36, 47, 48, 56, 71, **162**, 170, 183, 203, **204**
Bairstow Jim 99, 102, 213
Banana Two Piece 189; *see also* cable
Banda, Hastings 184
Bane, Maurice 8, 10, 50–1, 52, 57, 61, 78–9, 91–2, 94–5, 102, 130, 171, 173–4, 225, 228
banks 69, 82, 89, 212; *see also* Hong Kong
Barbados 7, 13, 14, 29, 103, 107, 143, 175, 176, 217, **218–19**, 261
  BET 176
  Bridgetown 144, 261
Bardens, Bertie 92, 94
Batavia *see* Indonesia
BBC 123, 247, 248
Bermuda 18, **19**, 32, 37, 73, 79, 82, 164, 168, 176, **188**, **206**
  St George's 164
Bird, John 185
Blue Books 169; *see also* Head Office: Engineering Department
Blundell, Herbie 73, 175-6, 200, 202
Bolivia 30, 181, 251
  La Paz 4, 30, 254–7
bonding 28, 32, 35, 83, 112, 213
Borneo 165
Bosdet, Patricia 31, 104, 106, 182, 187, 220
Botswana 197
  Teletswana 197
BP 83, 209
Bragg, John 30, 107–8, 150, 152, **153**, 243
Brazil 45, 83, 106, 110, 179, 181
  Belém do Para 46
  Recife 45, 60
  Rio de Janeiro 74, 110
British American Tobacco 107
British Telecom 214; *see also* Post Office
Brittenden, Victor 260
broadcasting 156, 207
Bruce, Bob 228
bureaucracy 216
Busch, Natusz 254

cable xv–xviii, 10, 29, 34, 46, 62, 66, 103, **111**, 112, 114, 119, 120, 127, 156, 161, 178, 193, 210, 244
  abandonment of 34, 115, 160
  balance 62
  cable chains 39, 62, 66, 115
  coaxial cables 157, 160, 163, 164, 205, 214, 239, 242
  end 43, **44**
  fibre optic 64, 163, 235
  land line 46, 248, 264
  pilot chain 159
  regenerator 39, 62, 160
  submarine cable 35, 36, 46, 123, 156, 157, 159, 160,

163, 179, 189, **206**, 224
telegram 64, 71, 157, 163, 164
see also COMPAC; SEACOM; telephone
Cable & Wireless
advertising **137**, **139**, **146–7**
Board (formerly Court) of Directors 28, 104, 185, 216, 221, 232
business systems 221
Cable & Wireless College, previously training school 3, 6, 7, 8, 13, 21, 29, 32, 214
Coventry 29, 32, 214
Hampstead Hill 3
Porthcurno 2, 6, 14, 21, **22–5**, 26, 28, 29, 30, 32, 64, 70, 87, 88, 96, 112, 132, 160, 214
see also Marconi
companies, *see individual company names*; Barbados, Botswana, Fiji, Trinidad
Exiles Club 117
Head Office 11, 28, 31, 35, 102, 104, **105**, 107, **135**, **137**, 159, 164, 170, 179, 182, 185, 187, 191, 199, 211, 216, 220, 242, 250
Chief Clerk 11, 31, 211
Engineering Department 159, 164, 165
Ships Section 31
Staff Department 11, 12, 182
Staff Manager 108
Traffic Department 11, 211
Traffic Manager 4
history of xvi-xix, 266, 267 *and passim*
Managing Director 173, 175, 220, 235
Officials 104
shares 220, 221; *see also* privatisation
Cable & Wireless Services 193
cable code 95, 157, 159, 160; *see also* Morse; 'five unit'
cable ship 31, 43, 66, **68**, 70, 73, 160-1, 183, 220, 262
cable laying **67**, **166**
cable station 7, 29, 34, **54**, 57, 64, 67, 75, 96, 103, 161, 171, 261
instrument room 26, **38**, **42**, 62, 176
instruments, 'polished brass and mahogany' 6, 61, 64, 120, 141, 161, 260
telegraph office 225
watches, 'on the rounds' 14, 57
Cable West Coast 181, 257
Cambodia 152
Canada 88
Cape of Good Hope 114
capital investment 156
Caribbean 31, 66, 86, 114, 123, 169, 175, 185, 189, 217; *see also individual islands*
Carrington, Paul 13-14, 217
Central America 195
centralisation 103; *see also* Cable & Wireless: Head Office
Ceylon 43, 99, 133, 134, 138
Colombo 12, 61, 94, 127, 138, 160
Ngombo 43
Trincomalee 140
Chad 140
children 78, 79, 80, 83, 85, 86, 118, 262
Chile 82, 179
Los Andes 264
Valparaiso 82
China 173, 209, 224, 235, 237, 239, 242, 243; *see also* Hong Kong
Beijing / Peking 235, 238, 242, 243
Hang Chow 238
Kwangtung / Canton 238, 240, 242, 244
Shanghai 224, 238
Shatin 240
Shenzhen 244
Chinese employees, skill of 40, 150, 232, 234, 236–7
Christmas Island 126
clock 61, **63**; *see also* cable station
clothing 46, 47
clubs 50, 53, 70, 75, 81, 83, 85, 89, 183, 225; *see also* expatriates; mess; social life
Cocos (Keeling) Islands 28, 66, 114, 115, 124–30, 133, 159
barrel ceremony 127, **128–9**
boating accident 130
Clunies-Ross family 114, 126
Direction Island 114, **125**, 127
Home Island 133
Tin Can Mail 126
Coll, Gustavo 26, 178–9, 181
Colonial Service 88
colonial ways 34, 70, 72, 88, 90, 91, 92, 94, 95, 96, 99, 104, 156, 182, 183
colonies, colonialism 169, 174; *see also individual countries*
informal empire 178
'wind of change' 88, 156; *see also* decolonisation, independence
Commonwealth 156, 184
COMPAC 237
competition 169, 178
computers 212
consolidation 14; *see also* training
construction 156
continuities over time 169
contract work 156, 194, 221; *see also* new business; SANGCOM
copra 126
corporate bond 20
Corrall, Ian 47, 56, 154, 210, 223, 228-9
Costains 194
cotton industry xvi, 40
coups 246, 248, 251, 254
Cowan, Pat 66, 70–1, 170–1, 181, 212, 235
Critchley, Peter **116**, 117
Crown Agents 30
Cuba 6, 238, 255
cyclone 127, 228
Cyprus 29
Czechoslovakia 173, 207

Darvill, Bob 14
Davenport, John 20–1, 53, 55, 62, 72, 81, 161, **162**, 163, 164–5, 203
Davies, Wilfred 175, 182
decolonisation 170; *see also* independence
Diego Garcia 114
digital 168, 235
doctor, medical attention 37, 47, 124
Doha 87, 183, 203
drink 52, 55, 61, 86, 89, 92, 94, 127, 199, 202, 203, 215, 240
drinking water 47, 57
Dublin 189

Dunne, Marie-Louise 71–2
Dunne, Tony 27, 71–2, 118–9

Eades, John 152
earth station *see* satellite
earthquake 82, 264
East Africa 89, 247
East African Federation 184
Eastern Extension Company 114
Eastern Telegraph Company 6, 34, 37, 39, 50, 56, 69, 79, 92, 95, 96, 104, 106, 254
  'Father Eastern' 95
economic depression, 1930s xvii, 3
Edinburgh, Duke of 64, **65**
Eggers, Henry 173, 182
Egypt 39, 189, 246
  Alexandria 40, **42**, 49, 69, 96, 246–7
  Aswan 52; *see also* Nile
  Cairo 140
  Suez 39, 51, 61, 96, 246
El Salvador 195
electromechanical equipment 61, 66; *see also* cable station: instruments
electronics 66, 164, 212
Empire 132, 169; *see also* colonies; Commonwealth
engineering 3, 178, *and passim*
engineering books 169
equipment 152
errors 159
ethos 35, 36, 95, 110, 112, 163
expatriates xv-xvi, 2, 88, 89, 157, 169, 173, 179, 181, 183, 197, 200, 211, 213, 214, 235, 266
  attitudes towards xvi, 35, 213
  see also clubs; F1; social life

F1, foreign service staff 34, 36, 40, 55, 108, 110, 145, 157, 176, 198, 203, 211, 213, *and passim*
facsimile 159
Falklands conflict 181
family 37, 39, 78, 95, 214, 225; *see also* children; marriage; romance
family connections 3, 6, 18, 45, 168; *see also* recruitment
Fanning Island 49, 91, 114
Farmer, Arthur 7, 143
Faroukh, King 246
Fiji 12, 182, 183
  FINTEL 182
  Suva 49, **166**
'five unit' 157, 159, 160; *see also* cable code
floods 228
food 49, 55, 83, 90, 127
formality 99
Foster, Paul 7, 13, 66, 68, 143–4, 261
franchises 156, 178, 181, 185, 196
'fraternising with the natives' 71–3; *see also* punishment; romance
Fuge, John 164, 168–9, 248–50
Fung Hak Ming 131, 235–7

gaol **142**, 143
GCHQ 123

Ghana 171, 173
  Accra **38**, 52, **54**, 136, 140
  Takaradi 136
GI Call Home Program 150, 152; *see also* Vietnam
Gibraltar 61, 72, 106
Gilkes, Sonny 176, 178
Gold Coast *see* Ghana
Grand Metropolitan 200
Great Britain
  Cornwall 28, 30, 32; *for* Porthcurno *see* Cable & Wireless
  Devon 27, 71
  Dorset 30
  government 216, 220
    Civil Service 123, 220
    Conservative administration xix, 216
    Department of Trade and Industry 216
    Foreign Office 37, 74, 194
    Labour administration 216
    Ministry of Defence 198
    Treasury xviii, 216
  Liverpool 40, 134
  London 2, 3, 8, 62, 102, 103, 165, 248, 257; *see also* Cable & Wireless: Head Office
    Embankment 4, 5, 11, 20, 27
    Moorgate 4
    Temple 8
  Penzance 26, 28
  Plymouth 27
Grenada 13, 191, 193
Guam 165, 237
Guatemala 195
guerrillas, terrorism 29, 145, 148
guided missile 120

Hardiman, Wally 106–7, 197–8
Hart-Davis, Duff xv
hierarchical system 21, 34, 95, 98, 104, 106, 211
  grades 98
  promotion 95, 106
Histed, Brenda 60, 83, 85, 214–15
Histed, Richard 45–6, 205
Hong Kong xviii-xix, 10, 31, 43, 78, 79, 80, 85, 86, 98, **100–1**, 102, 103, 108, 110, 123, 131, 150, 152, 163, 165, 171, 183, 185, 187, 193, 198, 212, 216, 217, 220, 222, 223-37, **226–7**, **230**, 243–4, **244**
  Aberdeen Harbour 231
  Bank of China 225, 228
  Cape d'Aguilar **233**
  Chartered Bank 228
  Chinese ways persisting 229
  Crown Colony 224, 229, 234
  growth of 228, 229, 232, 235, 244
  Hong Kong & Shanghai Bank 89, 228, 234
  Hong Kong Telephone Company 234, 236, 239
  Hong Kong–Canton Railway 239–40, **241**
  International Maintenance Centre 231
  Jardine Matheson 234
  Kowloon 225, 228, 231
  Legislative Council 234
  Mount Butler 85
  New Territories 231
  Radio Hong Kong 228

Stanley 237
traffic control 228
housing 43, 45, 46, 102, 106, 108, 123, 199, 200, 207, 232
Howie, John 4, 6, 51–2, 95–6, 245, 251–2, 254–7, 261–2, 264
hurricane 261, 262

ICI 83
ICL 212
illness 45, 50, 52, 53, 55, 140, 215
Imperial and International Communications xvii
independence 88, 156, 169, 170, 171–4, **172**, 194, 246, 247; *see also* colonies; *individual countries*
India 228
Bombay 194
Calcutta 96, 240
Indian Ocean 126
Indonesia
Bali 143
Banjawoengie 13, 189
Jakarta **84**, **142**, 143
Jurong 143
Medang 165
Telok Ayer 140
individualism 112
integrated circuits 165
intelligence 123, 134
International Telecommunications Union 196, 239
Iran 56
islands 114, 127; *see also individual islands*
Israel 15, 144; *see also* war: Arab–Jewish conflict; Palestine
Haifa 15, 145, 148
Jaffa 15, 145
Nablus 145
Tel Aviv 15, 148

Jamaica 73, 86, 262
Kingston **172**
Japan 205, 222, 235
Japanese 133, 140, 143, 235, 238
joint ventures 175

Kameran Island 92
Kenya 29, 247
Mombasa 27, 82
Nairobi 27, 29, 79, 159, 184, 247
Kenyatta, Jomo 247
Kipling, Rudyard 96
Kleyn, Howard 18, 20, 36, 53, 157, 159, 193–4, 229, 243–4
Knight, Alan 189
Korea 132
Kuwait **186**

Labuan **97**
Laos 152
Lebanese 85, 174
Leeward Islands 189
Leighton, Basil 36-7, 48, 52
liquor syndicates 203; *see also* drink
Lloyds Bank 107
Lloyd's signal station 161
local staff 13, 47, 88, 89, 103, 169, 174, 175, 176, 183, 197, 203, 235
localisation 236
Lorens, Albert 15–16, 18, 145, 148, 160

Macao 205
Malawi 184
Malaya 141
Port Dixon 143
Maldive Islands 210
male dominance 211; *see also* hierarchical system; women, employment of
malnutrition 210; *see also* illness
Malta 61, 96
Mao Tse-Tung 238
March-Penney, Janet 73–4, **76–7**, 85
March-Penney, John 73, **76–7**
Marconi College, Chelmsford 10, 123
Marconi Company xvii, 123, 184, 189
Marcos, President 205
marriage 2, 28, 45, 69, 70, 73, 74, 75, 85, 86, 106; *see also* romance
Maugham, W. Somerset xv, 94
Mauritius 27, 66, 70, 71, 114, 159
Port Louis 159
Mediterranean 61
Mercury Communications xix, 18, 157, 221, 222
Mesa, Garcia 256, 257
mess 29, 34, 37, 39, 43, 50, 56, 70, 72, 94, 95, 96, 106, 127, 171, 200
message-switching 212
messengers 15
Metal Box 18
microwave 189, 197
Middle East 89, 187, 189, 228; *see also* Arabian Gulf; *individual countries*
military governments 179; *see also* coups
Miller & Corey 57
mirror galvanometer 66; *see also* cable station: instruments
missionaries 49, 50, 55, 89, 214
money 141
monopolies 170, 196
Montserrat 86
Moore, Derek 18, 74, 86–7, 98–9, 115, 117–18, 127
Moore, Elizabeth 74, 80, 86–7, 98–9, 115, 117–18
Morse 3, 7, 27, 134; *see also* cable code; digital
Moulson, Peter 33
Muscat 53, 55, 56, 72, **111**, **177**
Muttra 53
mutinies 247

Napoleon 115
NASA 123, 210
space mission Apollo 120, 122, 123, **188**
space mission Gemini 120
Nash, John 126–7, 251
Nasser, Gamal Abdul 246
National Service 36
nationalisation xvii, 179, 181, 217
Nepal 152

Netherlands 136, 191
New Guinea 165
New Zealand 12, 99, 143, 234
new business, diversification xviii-xix, 28, 156, 187, 189, 193, 224, 258
news agencies 228
Nigeria 140, 173, 175
  Kano 175
  Lagos 140, 173, 175
  Nigerian External Telecoms 175
Nile, River **41**, 52
Nkrumah, Kwame 173
North Africa 134
North Borneo 40, 90
  Jesselton 40, 43, **44**, **167**
Nyerere, Julius 247

Obote, Milton 247
oil companies 200, 203
Olsen, Rod 221–2, 234–5
operators 3, 13, 40, 47, 66, 72, 94, 96, 143, 144, 159, 176, 179, 246, 247
  laying-off 3
Optus 30
oral history xix-xxii
Organization of American States 254
OTC 12

Pacific 169, 196, 205, 235
Pacific Cable Board 12
Packer, John 64, 68, 88–90, 119–20, 122
Pakistan 53, 56
  Karachi 53, 140
Palestine 15, 144, 148; *see also* Israel; war: Arab–Jewish conflict
PanAm 228
paper tape 6
Parker, Tony xxii
partnership 156, 169, 170, 175, 178, 182, 185
paternalism 21, 95
patriarchalism 34
pay 37, 106, 107, 108, 110, 175, 200, 211, 212
Pemberton, Brian 28, 170, 183–5, 188, 232, 234, 247
Penang 61, 143
Pender, Sir John xvi-xvii
pension 37
Perim 161
Perón, Juan 21, 251
Peronistas 251
Peru 179, 181, 264
  Lima **76–7**, 181
  Mollendo **63**
Philippines 8, 205, 214
  Manila 8, 150, 205, 214
phosphates 126
physical threats 246
political instability 156, 169, 178, 246; *see also* coups
politics 176, 178
Pope, George 40
Portugal 75
  Carcavelos 74, 75
  Lisbon 45, 79

Post Office xvii–xviii, 4, 240; *see also* British Telecom
press 247, 260, 261
Press Ship 140, 141; *see also* TELCOM
private business services 183, 185, 232
privatisation xix, 157, 214, 216, 217, 220, 221, 234, 235
profits 182
public ownership 34, 216; *see also* nationalisation
Puerto Rico 73, 144
punishment 53, 70, 108, 115, 72

Qatar 203

race relations 72, 73, 173–4
radio 7, 10, 14, 29, 34, 43, 47, 114, 143, 156, 157, **158**, 160, 161, 171, 225, 238; *see also* telephone
  amateur radio 13
  HF radio 119, 152, 163, 183, 194, 195, 199, 217, 247
  Military Amateur Radio System 150
  radio station 85, 98, 210, 248
  radio telephone 164
  ship-to-shore 248
  TORS, Teleprinter On Radio 173
  tropospheric scatter **162**, 183, 197, **233**
  VHF 199, 242
  wide-band 212
railways 69, 179, 238–40; *see also* travel by rail
recruitment 3, **9**, 20, 28, 30; *see also* training
Red Sea 61, 92, 160, 161
  'Cook's Tour' 96
Reece, Ken 103–4
religion 82; *see also* missionaries
remoteness 49; *see also* islands
retirement 14, 52, **76–7**, 108
return home 60, 108; *see also* expatriates
revenue 171, 228
revolutions 246; *see also* coups; *individual countries*
Rhodesia 184
  Salisbury 184
riots 236
Rippengal, John 35, 134, 136, 138, 140–1, 150, 237–9
Rodrigues 66, 70, 114, 170, 171
romance 28, 69, 73, 200; *see also* marriage
romanticism 57
rules and regulations 36; *see also* F1
Russia (USSR) 161, 173, 174

Saba 189-91, **192**, 193
Sabah, *see* North Borneo
St Croix 66
St Helena 115, 118
St Kitts 66, **158**
St Lucia 13, 144
St Martin 189
St Thomas 114
St Vincent [Cape Verde Islands] 56, **58–9**, 81, 114
St Vincent [West Indies] **180**
SANGCOM xviii, 197–202, **201**, 221; *see also* Saudi Arabia
satellite 34, 114, 120, 122, 123, 152, 156, 157, 160, 163, 165, 168, 171, 179, 189, 194, 243
  earth station 120, 122, 160, 165, 178, 181, 182, **186**, 189, 195, 210, **218–19**, 236, 237, 243

Saudi Arabia 197, 198, 199, 200, 205
Ar Ar 199, 200
Damman 200
Dhahran 199
Jeddah 199, 200
Nejran 199, 200
Riyadh 198, 199, 200
Taif 199, 200
Schofield, Chris 49–50, 91, 209, 246–7
schooling 3, 27, 30, 31, 78, 79; *see also* children; recruitment
SEACOM 165, **166–7**, 237
secondment 184
security of tenure, 'job for life' 36, 37, 107
Selby, Richard 32, 60, 82, 207, 209, 221
seniority 95, 98, 99, 102, 104; *see also* hierarchical system: grade
servants 96, 108, **109**, 117
service ethos 36, 110, 217
Services *see* armed forces
Seychelles 61, 81, 106, 159, 160, 194–5
Shackleton, Sir Ernest 57
Sharp, Colin 1, 55, 194–5
Shell 18, 57, 83, 107, 185
Sherwood, Joan 183, 213
Sherwood, Sidney 183
ship watch 143
short-term staff, short tours of duty 211, 214
Sierra Leone 173, 248–51
Freetown 248, 251
Singapore 43, 61, 62, 106, 126, 130, 133, 140, 143, 165, 170, 189, 228, 235
Skoda 207
Slaughter, John 155, 189–91, 193, 195–7, **196**, 258
Smith, Ian 184
Smith, Noel 160–1
snipers 145
social life 36, 50, 57, 69, 71, 72, 81, 82, 83, **84**, 86, 87, 90, 91, 199, 200, 209, 213, 231, 237, 238; *see also* expatriates; F1
Solomon Islands 88, 89, 182
Honiara 90
South Africa 66, 88, 254
South America xviii, 55, 88, 106, 156, 169, 178, 179, 181, 214, 246, 251; *see also individual countries*
South-East Asia 150, 205, 214, 221, 243; *see also individual countries*
space ventures 114, 120; *see also* NASA; satellite
special services 183, 229; *see also* Cable & Wireless Services; new business; private business services
sport 6, 20, 27, 39, 43, 50, 61, 89, 126, 127, 144, 175, 176, 183, 212
World Cup 212
Sri Lanka *see* Ceylon
Stubbs, Colin 12-13, 70, 82, 143
Suart, Brian 40, 43, 47, 71, 85, 86, 98, 115, 138, 141, 143, 242–3
Suart, Wendy 40, 43, 71, 81, 85-6, 90–1, 98, 108, 110, 229, 231
Sudan 140
Port Sudan 39, 50, 51, 57, 61, 70, 95, 96, 161
Suez Crisis 27, 246
Sumatra 133, 140

Taiwan 235
Tanganyika 247; *see also* Tanzania; Zanzibar
tanks 252
Tanzania 258, **259**
Dar-es-Salaam 159
Taylor Woodrow 197
technological change 3, 35, 157; *see also* cable; radio; satellite
TELCOM 12, 99, 132, 134, 141, 143, 144, 150, 213; *see also* war
telephone 34, 120, 152, 156, 163, **201**, 203, 238, 242, 257
walkie-talkie 184
telephone cables 64, 171; *see also* cable: submarine, coaxial, fibre optic
telephone exchange **180**, 184, 194, 195
telephone systems 190, 196
telephone terminal unit, TTU 164
teleprinter 110, 159, 217
TORS *see* radio
television 191
telex 152, 159, 165, 212, 216, 217, 228
terrorism 145, 148, 154
Thailand 152
Thompson, Paul xxii
Tibet 238
Tortola 190
training 2–32, **16–17**, 35, 175, 178, 202; *see also* Cable & Wireless College
examinations, tests 6
General Examination 36
travel by air xv, 49, 79, 80, 82, 92, 103, 115, 120, 136, 152, 165, 212, 228, 258
travel by rail 26, 51, 60, 240, 264
travel by road 130, 239, 240, 249, 252
travel by sea 21, 27, 30, 49, 51, 56, 79, 94, 117, 118, 119, 124, 126, 127, 136, 225, 228, 250
Trinidad 144, 178
TEXTEL, Trinidad and Tobago External Telecoms 178
Turks and Caicos Islands 210
Tunnels 29; *see* Cable & Wireless: training: Porthcurno

Uganda 247, 258
Entebbe 258
Kampala 247, 258
United Nations 30, 210
Uruguay 178, 179
Montevideo 26, 55, 178, 179, 181
USA 73, 114, 152, 168, 173, 176, 193, 243, 247
Americans 118, 119, 120
Miami 262
New York 110, 164, 257
Oakland 152

Washington DC 176
see also NASA
Vietnam 132, 150, **151**, 152, **153**, 243
Saigon 152
Vincent, Eric 240
volcano 260

war, wartime xvii, 4, 7, 8, 10, 11, 13, 14, 40, 50, 51, 99, 114, 131–54, 235; *see also* armed forces; TELCOM
Arab–Jewish conflict 132, 144-8, **149**
Boer War 66
both World Wars 115
civil war 195
convoys 4, 136, 140
Korean War 144
Second World War 35, 115, 122, 124, 131–44, 213
submarines 134, 143, 144
Vietnam 150–2, **151**, **153**
Zipper operation 140, 141
Warren, Keith 45, 124, 126, 132
Warren, Pat 45
Warwick, George 10, 37, 43, 45, 103, 113, 163, 171, 216–17, 217, 220
Werngren, Ron 21, 26, 69, 110, 112, 181, 198–9, 231–2, 266
West Africa 52, 89, 171, 248; *see also individual countries*
West Indies *see* Caribbean
Westec (Western Technical Services) 181
Western Telegraph Company 21, 34, 69, 106, 156, 178, 179
Willett, Archie 175, 220
Wilshaw, Sir Edward 8, 132
Wilson, R. 'Tug' 191
wireless *see* radio
withdrawal 182; *see also* decolonisation; independence
Wolfe, Pete 3–4, 108, 124, 133–4
women, employment of 12, 31, 211–12; *see also* marriage
women's rights 211
Wood, Arthur 237, 238
Woods, Brian 30, 82
Worrall, John 29, 122–3, 165, 168, 178, 214

Yemen, North and South 154, 207–9; *see also* Aden
Sana'a 154, 207–9, **208**

Zanzibar 30, 72, 79, 82, 159